TEXAS Student Interactive

myView
LITERACY
K

SAVVAS
LEARNING COMPANY

ISBN-13: 978-0-328-94158-2
ISBN-10: 0-328-94158-1

9 2021

Julie Coiro, Ph.D.

Jim Cummins, Ph.D.

Pat Cunningham, Ph.D.

Elfrieda Hiebert, Ph.D.

Pamela Mason, Ed.D.

Ernest Morrell, Ph.D.

P. David Pearson, Ph.D.

Frank Serafini, Ph.D.

Alfred Tatum, Ph.D.

Sharon Vaughn, Ph.D.

Judy Wallis, Ed.D.

Lee Wright, Ed.D.

Going Places

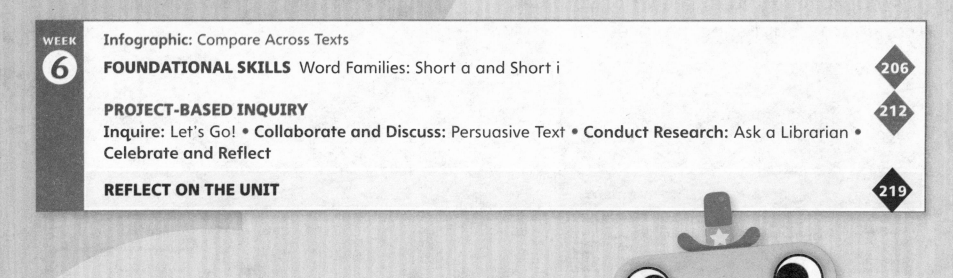

Going Places

Essential Question

What makes a place special?

 Watch

"**My Community**" and see what you can learn about special places.

 TURN *and* **TALK**

What places are in your community?

SAVVAS
realize™
Go ONLINE for
all lessons.

 VIDEO

AUDIO

 GAME

 ANNOTATE

 BOOK

RESEARCH

Reading Workshop

Reading-Writing Bridge

• Academic Vocabulary • Pre-Spelling • Read Like a   **Realistic Fiction**
Writer, Write for a Reader • Language and Conventions

Writing Workshop

• Independent Writing and Conferences • Meet the Author • When to Start a New Book
• Make and Respond to Suggestions • Publish and Celebrate

Project-Based Inquiry

Write an Opinion   **Persuasive Text**

Independent Reading

You can learn to be a good reader!

1. Choose a book.

2. Hold it right side up.

3. Start at the front cover.

4. Turn the pages carefully.

TEKS K.2.D.i Identify the front cover, back cover, and title page of a book; **TEKS K.2.D.ii** Hold a book right side up, turn pages correctly, and know that reading moves from top to bottom and left to right with return sweep; **TEKS K.4.A** Self-select text and interact independently with text for increasing periods of time.

Directions Discuss the steps for reading with students. Say: Pick a book that looks interesting. Look through the book to make sure it is not too easy or too hard. Show a book and model how to identify the front cover, back cover, and title page. Then model how to hold the book right side up and turn pages correctly. Finally, model how to read from left to right and from top to bottom, including return sweep.

My Independent Reading Log

Date	Book	Pages Read	My Ratings
			☺ 😐 ☹
			☺ 😐 ☹
			☺ 😐 ☹
			☺ 😐 ☹

⭐ **TEKS K.2.D.i** Identify the front cover, back cover, and title page of a book; **TEKS K.2.D.ii** Hold a book right side up, turn pages correctly, and know that reading moves from top to bottom and left to right with return sweep; **TEKS K.4.A** Self-select text and interact independently with text for increasing periods of time. **ELPS 2.I.iii Listening**

Directions Have students self-select a text to read independently. Ask them to identify the front cover, back cover, and title page of the book. Then ask them to read the book correctly by holding it right side up and turning the pages carefully as they read from left to right and from top to bottom. Finally, have students complete the chart to tell about their independent reading.

Unit Goals

In this unit, you will

- ○ read fiction texts
- △ draw or write a text
- □ talk about what makes a place special

 MY TURN Color

Directions Read aloud the unit goals to students. Then ask them to identify the place in the picture and talk about what makes the place special. Have students color the picture.

Academic Vocabulary

map	move	land	special

A park is a **special** place. 👍 👎

It is fun to **move** to a new place. 👍 👎

A **map** is a helpful tool. 👍 👎

I like to plant things in the **land**. 👍 👎

TURN and TALK Talk about your answers.

🔷 **TEKS K.6.F** Respond using newly acquired vocabulary as appropriate. **ELPS 1.A.ii Learning; 2.C.iv Listening; 3.D.ii Speaking; 4.C.iii Reading**

Directions Read aloud the Academic Vocabulary words and the sentences to students. Have students color the thumbs up if they agree with the statement and the thumbs down if they do not agree. Then have students use the newly acquired Academic Vocabulary to talk about their responses with a partner.

Read Together

Using Your Imagination

You can use your imagination when you play.

14

Weekly Question

How does imagination make a place seem different?

You can write about the places you imagine.

 TURN and **TALK** Where do you go in your imagination?

🔵 **TEKS K.6.E** Interact with sources in meaningful ways such as illustrating or writing. **ELPS 2.I.iii Listening; 3.E.i Speaking**

Directions Read the text to students. Then have them interact with the source by looking at the pictures and text and talking about how they can use their imaginations to go places.

Initial Sounds

 SEE and SAY Circle

TEKS K.2.A Demonstrate phonological awareness. **ELPS 2.I.iii Listening**

Directions Have students demonstrate phonological awareness by circling the picture word in each pair that begins with the sound /m/. Model: Listen to the beginning sounds in these words: /m/ -*ouse*, /k/ -*at*. The word *mouse* begins with the sound /m/.

Consonant Mm

🔴 **TEKS K.2.B.i** Identify and match the common sounds that letters represent; **TEKS K.2.E** Develop handwriting by accurately forming all uppercase and lowercase letters using appropriate directionality. **ELPS 4.C.i Reading; 5.A.i Writing**

Directions Tell students that the letter *m* can make the sound /m/. Model how to form the letters *M* and *m*. Say: You will see the letter *m* in many words that have the sound /m/. Trace the letters *Mm*. Point to the letter *m* and identify, or tell me, the sound it makes. Now you will match the letters and the sound. Circle each picture that has the sound for *m* at the beginning.

17

Consonant Mm

 MY TURN Write

18

⭐ **TEKS K.2.B.i** Identify and match the common sounds that letters represent. **ELPS 4.C.i Reading; 5.A.i Writing**

Directions Have students say each picture word and identify the beginning sound. Say: If the word begins with the sound /m/, write the letters *Mm* on the lines.

Initial and Final Sounds

 SEE and SAY (Circle)

 TEKS K.2.A Demonstrate phonological awareness. **ELPS 1.C.i Learning; 2.I.iii Listening**

Directions Say: Listen to the sound at the beginning of this word: /t/ -*ire*. The beginning sound is /t/. Have students demonstrate phonological awareness by circling the picture words in the first row that begin with the same sound as *tire* and the picture words in the second row that end with the same sound as *pot*.

Consonant Tt

 Circle

★ **TEKS K.2.B.i** Identify and match the common sounds that letters represent; **TEKS K.2.E** Develop handwriting by accurately forming all uppercase and lowercase letters using appropriate directionality. **ELPS 4.C.i Reading; 5.A.i Writing**

Directions Tell students that the letter *t* can make the sound /t/. Say: You will see the letter *t* in many words that have the sound /t/. Model how to form the letters *T* and *t*. Have students trace the letters *Tt* and identify the sound that *t* makes. Then have them match the letters and sound by circling the picture words in the first row that begin with the sound for *t* and the picture words in the second row that end with the sound for *t*.

My Words to Know

I	am	the

My Sentences to Read

 MY TURN

 I am the mouse.

 I am the lion.

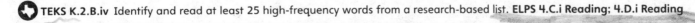

TEKS K.2.B.iv Identify and read at least 25 high-frequency words from a research-based list. **ELPS 4.C.i Reading; 4.D.i Reading**

Directions Say: There are some words that we have to remember and practice. Listen as I read these words: *I, am, the.* Have students read the high-frequency words. Then say: You can identify, or find, the words in sentences. Ask students to look at the sentences and underline the high-frequency words. Then have them read the sentences.

Consonant Tt

 Write

22

TEKS K.2.B.i Identify and match the common sounds that letters represent. **ELPS 4.C.i Reading; 5.A.i Writing**

Directions Say: Remember that the letter *t* makes the sound /t/. Have students write the letters *Tt* on the lines and identify the sound that *t* makes. Then have them draw lines to match the letters to the picture words that begin or end with the sound for *t*.

I Am

Highlight the words with the **m** sound.

 AUDIO

Audio with Highlighting

 ANNOTATE

 I am the man.

 TEKS K.2.B.i Identify and match the common sounds that letters represent; **TEKS K.2.B.iv** Identify and read at least 25 high-frequency words from a research-based list. **ELPS 4.C.iv Reading; 4.D.i Reading**

I am the monkey.

I am the turkey.

24

🌟 **TEKS K.2.B.i** Identify and match the common sounds that letters represent; **TEKS K.2.B.iv** Identify and read at least 25 high-frequency words from a research-based list. **ELPS 4.C.iv Reading; 4.D.i Reading**

Underline the words with the **t** sound.

 I am the tiger.

⭐ **TEKS K.2.B.i** Identify and match the common sounds that letters represent; **TEKS K.2.B.iv** Identify and read at least 25 high-frequency words from a research-based list. **ELPS 4.C.iv Reading; 4.D.i Reading**

Consonants Mm and Tt

 Say

 map **man** **mop**

top **ten** **rat**

26

TEKS K.2.B.i Identify and match the common sounds that letters represent. **ELPS 3.B.ii Speaking**

Directions Remind students that the letter *m* makes the sound /m/ and the letter *t* makes the sound /t/. Have partners take turns pointing to the *m* or *t* in each word and saying the sound for the letter. Then have them use the picture to identify each word.

Consonants Mm and Tt

 Circle

I am the monkey.　　(Mm)　　Tt

I am the turkey.　　Mm　　Tt

I am the tiger.　　Mm　　Tt

I am the mouse.　　Mm　　Tt

 TEKS K.2.B.i Identify and match the common sounds that letters represent; **TEKS K.2.B.iv** Identify and read at least 25 high-frequency words from a research-based list. **ELPS 4.C.i Reading; 4.C.iv Reading**

Directions Have students read the sentences. Ask them to circle the letters that match the beginning sound of the animal name in each sentence.

My Learning Goal

I can read realistic fiction.

SPOTLIGHT ON GENRE

Realistic Fiction

Realistic fiction is a story that could happen in real life.

Characters	Look at Tim and Jan.
Setting	They go to school.
Plot	They read. They color. They play together!

TURN and TALK Talk about how you know this story is realistic fiction.

TEKS K.7.B Identify and describe the main character(s); TEKS K.7.C Describe the elements of plot development, including the main events, the problem, and the resolution for texts read aloud with adult assistance; TEKS K.7.D Describe the setting. ELPS 2.D.ii Listening; 3.B.ii Speaking; 4.G.iii Reading

Directions Say: Characters are the people or animals in a story. Setting is where and when a story takes place. Plot is what happens, or the main events, in a story. Have students identify and describe the characters, setting, and plot in the model text. Then have them discuss how they know it is realistic fiction.

28

Realistic Fiction
Anchor Chart

Characters

Setting

Events

1

2

3

Mission Accomplished!

Preview Vocabulary

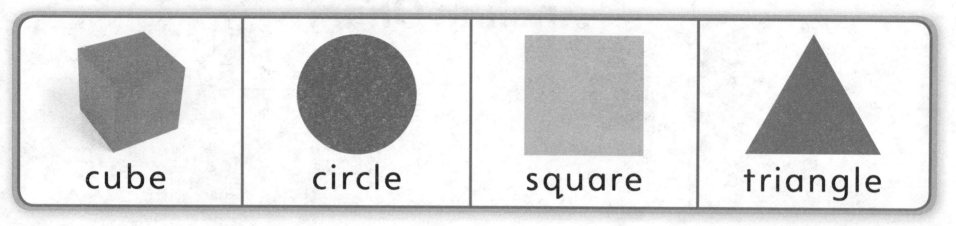

| cube | circle | square | triangle |

Read

Read the story to find out what the characters do.

Use prereading supports to enhance comprehension of written text. **ELPS 4.D.1 Reading**

Meet *the* Author

Ebony Joy Wilkins writes books for children and schools. She used to be a teacher. She likes traveling, playing tennis, and visiting her family.

30

Mission Accomplished!

written by Ebony Joy Wilkins
illustrated by Kevin Zimmer

 AUDIO

Audio with Highlighting

 ANNOTATE

Rena, we need more rocks!
Where can we find some?

CLOSE READ

Underline the name of the girl in the story.

I know where.
We can go to Mars.

33

🤠 **TEKS K.7.B** Identify and describe the main character(s). **ELPS 4.G.iii Reading**

Buckle up, Christopher.
Mars, here we come!

34

CLOSE READ

Underline the name of the boy in the story.

This rock is shaped like a cube.
I'll take it.

35

TEKS K.7.B Identify and describe the main character(s). ELPS 4.G.iii Reading

This rock is shaped like a circle.
I'll take it.

This rock is shaped like a square.
I'll take it.

This rock is shaped like a triangle.
But there's no room.

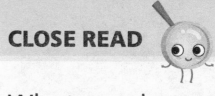
What word can you use to describe Rena and Christopher? Highlight words in the story that make you think this.

I have room.
Mission accomplished!
Let's go home.

39

TEKS K.6.C Use text evidence to support an appropriate response. **ELPS 4.G.iii** Reading

Develop Vocabulary

 MY TURN Match

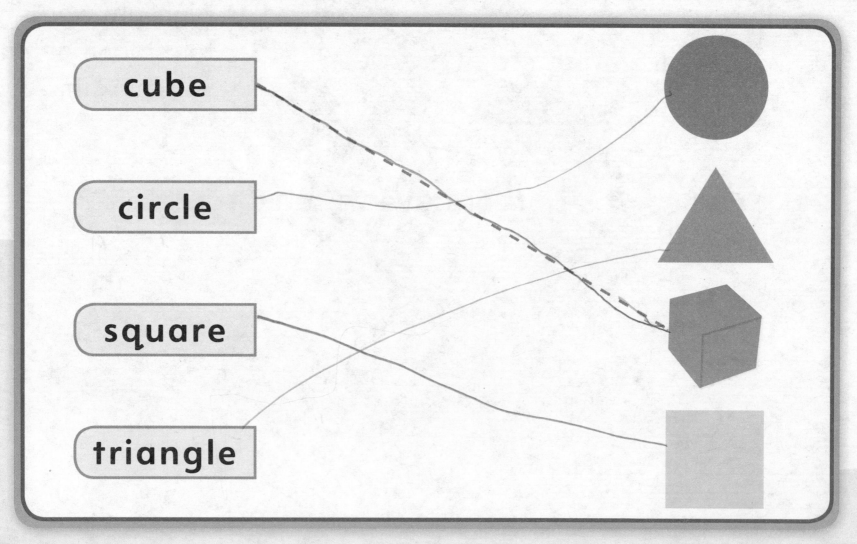

cube

circle

square

triangle

⭐ **TEKS K.3.B** Use illustrations and texts the student is able to read or hear to learn or clarify word meanings. **ELPS 2.I.iii Listening; 4.G.iii Reading**

40

Directions Read the vocabulary words to students. Then have them use illustrations to clarify the meanings of the words by drawing a line from each word to the matching picture.

Check for Understanding miamora

 MY TURN (Circle) and write

1. Where does the story happen?

park   **home**

2. Why does the author have the children go home?

The Love

3. What do the children do?

collected ROCKS

TEKS K.7.C Describe the elements of plot development including the main events, the problem, and the resolution for texts read aloud with adult assistance; **TEKS K.7.D** Describe the setting. **ELPS 2.I.iii Listening; 4.G.iii Reading; 5.G.iii Writing**

Directions Read question 1 and the answer choices aloud to students. Have them circle the answer. Then read questions 2 and 3 and have students write their answers.

41

Read Together

Identify and Describe Characters

Characters are 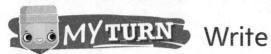 the people or animals in a story.

The **main characters** are who a story is mostly about.

 MY TURN Write

ReNov

ChRIStoPheR

42

TEKS K.7.B Identify and describe the main character(s). **ELPS 2.I.iii Listening; 4.G.iii Reading; 5.G.iii Writing**

Directions Read the information to students. Have them look back at the text and identify the main characters. Then have students write the characters' names next to their pictures.

Use Text Evidence

MY TURN Draw

TEKS K.6.C Use text evidence to support an appropriate response; **TEKS K.7.B** Identify and describe the main character(s). **ELPS 2.I.iii Listening; 4.G.iii Reading**

Directions Say: You can use details, or evidence, in a story to tell about the characters. Have students describe the main characters by drawing pictures of them. Remind students to look back at the text. Encourage them to look for details about the characters to add to their pictures.

Reflect and Share

 MY TURN Draw

Weekly Question

How does imagination make a place seem different?

⭐ **TEKS K.5.E** Make connections to personal experiences, ideas in other texts, and society with adult assistance; **TEKS K.6.B** Provide an oral, pictorial, or written response to a text; **TEKS K.6.E** Interact with sources in meaningful ways such as illustrating or writing. **ELPS 2.I.iii Listening; 4.G.iii Reading**

44

Directions Tell students they read about characters who collect rocks together. Ask them to think of other characters they have read about. Have students respond to sources by drawing a picture of Rena or Christopher and a character from another story.

Read Together

I can use words to tell about stories.

My Learning Goal

Academic Vocabulary

| map | move | land | special |

 MY TURN (Circle) and match

moves

remove

TEKS K.6.F Respond using newly acquired vocabulary as appropriate. **ELPS 4.F.iii Reading**

Directions Remind students that word parts can be added to words to make new words. Read each word and ask students to circle the word part that was added to the word *move*. Then have students draw a line from each word to the matching picture.

45

Concept Sort

 Circle

⭐ **TEKS K.3.C** Identify and use words that name actions; directions; positions; sequences; categories such as colors, shapes, and textures; and locations.
ELPS 2.I.iii Listening; 5.G.iii Writing

46

Directions Have students name the pictures and circle the picture words for animals. Then have students use the words to talk about the category. Ask: How are the circled picture words alike?

Read Like a Writer, Write for a Reader

 MY TURN Write

1. Find two words in the story that help you picture what the rocks look like.

_____

- -

_____

2. What other word can you use to tell what a rock looks like?

_____

- -

_____

TEKS K.9.D Discuss with adult assistance how the author uses words that help the reader visualize. **TEKS K.9.E** Listen to and experience first- and third-person texts. **ELPS 2.I.iii Listening; 3.F.ii Speaking**

Directions Say: We can experience a story by picturing it in our minds. Authors use words that help readers visualize, or picture in their minds what is happening. Read aloud pp. 35–38 as students picture the events in their minds. Read the items and have students write and discuss their responses.

Read Together

Singular Nouns

A **noun** can name a person
or an animal.

girl

dog

 TURN and **TALK** Say other words you know
that name a person or an animal.

 MY TURN Write

cat	boy

_____

- -

The _____ reads a book.

TEKS K.10.D.iii Edit drafts with adult assistance using standard English conventions, including singular and plural nouns. **ELPS 5.B.ii Writing**

48

Directions Read the information at the top of the page and explain that a singular noun names each one. Have students talk with a partner about other nouns for people and animals. Then have students edit the sentence by writing the correct singular noun on the lines.

Read Together

I can draw or write.

My Learning Goal

Introduction to Writing Workshop

Think about your favorite book.

Have you ever thought about who wrote it?

An **author** is someone who writes a book.

TURN and TALK Think like an author.

What books could you write?

You can be an author too!

TEKS K.10.A Plan by generating ideas for writing through class discussions and drawings. **ELPS 3.D.i Speaking**

Directions Have partners discuss their ideas about books they can write. Remind them to speak clearly as they share ideas with their partner.

What Good Writers Do

Writing Workshop will help you learn to be a good writer.

 Match

1. I will learn.

2. I will write.

3. I will talk.

4. I will share.

Directions Discuss with students how they should act during each part of the Writing Workshop. Then have students draw lines from each part of the Writing Workshop to the appropriate action.

Independent Writing and Conferences

How will you write on your own?

Think of ideas.	Choose an idea.	Write about it!

How will you talk about your writing?

☐ Ask questions. ☐ Listen actively.

☐ Share ideas. ☐ Stay on topic.

TURN and TALK Tell what you should do when you write on your own. Tell what you should do when you talk about your writing.

Directions Discuss with students what they are expected to do during independent writing and conferences. Then ask students to talk about what they should do during independent writing and conferences with a partner.

A New Place

I pack my toys and books.

Look at all that space!

I wonder what it will be like

To live in a new place.

old house

52

What is exciting about moving to a new place?

We pull up on the street,
And look at what we see!
Boys and girls are playing.
Will they be friends with me?

new house

TURN and TALK Talk about the poem.

What did you learn about moving to a new place?

⭐ **TEKS K.6.E** Interact with sources in meaningful ways such as illustrating or writing. **ELPS 2.I.iii Listening; 3.E.i Speaking**

Directions Read the poem to students. Then have them interact with the source by discussing how the author feels about moving to a new place and why. Ask students to tell what they learned about moving to a new place.

Middle Sounds

  Circle

⭐ **TEKS K.2.A** Demonstrate phonological awareness. **ELPS 2.I.iii Listening**

54

Directions Model: Listen to the sounds in *sack*: /s/ /a/ /k/. *Sack* has the sound /a/ in the middle. Have students demonstrate phonological awareness by saying the sounds in each picture word and circling the ones with /a/ in the middle.

Short a Spelled a

MY TURN (Circle)

⭐ **TEKS K.2.B.i** Identify and match the common sounds that letters represent; **TEKS K.2.E** Develop handwriting by accurately forming all uppercase and lowercase letters using appropriate directionality. **ELPS 4.C.i Reading; 5.A.i Writing**

Directions Tell students that the letter *a* can make the sound /a/. Model how to form the letters *A* and *a*. Then say: You will see the letter *a* in many words that have the short *a* sound. Point to the letter *a* and tell me the sound it makes. Now say each picture word and circle the pictures that have the short *a* sound in the middle. Write the letters *Aa* next to the pictures that have the short *a* sound.

55

Short a Spelled a

 Write

 map   Map

 mat   mat

 bat   bat

⭐ **TEKS K.2.B.i** Identify and match the common sounds that letters represent. **ELPS 4.C.i Reading; 5.A.i Writing**

Directions Have students trace the letter *a* in each word. Then ask them to identify and say the sounds for the letters they know in each word and write the letters on the lines. Finally, have students use the picture to identify and say each word.

Alliteration

 SEE and SAY <u>Underline</u>

 TEKS K.2.A.ii Recognize spoken alliteration or groups of words that begin with the same spoken onset or initial sound. **ELPS 1.C.i Learning; 2.I.iii Listening**

Directions Say: Some groups of words, such as *ant*, *ask*, and *apple*, begin with the same sound. Listen to this word: /s/-*un*, *sun*. Which picture words in the first row begin with the same sound as *sun*? Have students recognize spoken alliteration by underlining the picture words in the first row with the same initial sound. Continue with the second row.

Consonant Ss

  Underline

 TEKS K.2.B.i Identify and match the common sounds that letters represent; **TEKS K.2.E** Develop handwriting by accurately forming all uppercase and lowercase letters using appropriate directionality. **ELPS 4.C.i Reading; 5.A.i Writing**

58

Directions Tell students that the letter *s* can make the sound /s/. Model how to form the letters *S* and *s*. Then say: You will see the letter *s* in many words that have the /s/ sound. Trace the letters *Ss*. Point to the letter *s* and tell me the sound it makes. Now underline the picture word in each row that begins with the sound for *s*.

My Words to Know

a	to	like

My Sentences to Read

MY TURN

I like to bat.

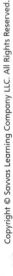

I like a mitt.

⭐ **TEKS K.2.B.iv** Identify and read at least 25 high-frequency words from a research-based list. **ELPS 4.C.iv Reading; 4.D.i Reading**

Directions Model: There are some words that we have to remember and practice. Listen as I read these words: *a, to, like*. Have students read the high-frequency words. Then say: You can identify, or find, the words in sentences. Look at the sentences and underline the words *a, to,* and *like*. Have students read the sentences.

Consonant Ss

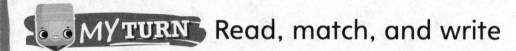 **Read, match, and write**

Sam

sat

Sa lm sat

60

⭐ **TEKS K.2.B.ii** Use letter-sound relationships to decode, including VC, CVC, CCVC, and CVCC words. **ELPS 4.C.i Reading; 5.A.i Writing**

Directions Remind students that the letter *s* can make the sound /s/. Say: Use what you know about letters and sounds to read each word. Then draw a line from each word to the matching picture. After students match the words to the pictures, have them choose one of the words to write on the lines.

Sam Sat

Highlight the words with the **s** sound.

 AUDIO

Audio with Highlighting

ANNOTATE

I am Sam.

TEKS K.2.B.i Identify and match the common sounds that letters represent; TEKS K.2.B.ii Use letter-sound relationships to decode, including VC, CVC, CCVC, and CVCC words; TEKS K.2.B.iv Identify and read at least 25 high-frequency words from a research-based list. ELPS 4.C.i Reading; 4.D.i Reading

I like to sit.

I like a m<u>a</u><u>t</u>.

TEKS K.2.B.i Identify and match the common sounds that letters represent; **TEKS K.2.B.ii** Use letter-sound relationships to decode, including VC, CVC, CCVC, and CVCC words; **TEKS K.2.B.iv** Identify and read at least 25 high-frequency words from a research-based list. **ELPS 4.C.iv Reading; 4.D.i Reading**

Underline the words with the short **a** sound.

Sam sat at the mat.

TEKS K.2.B.i Identify and match the common sounds that letters represent; **TEKS K.2.B.ii** Use letter-sound relationships to decode, including VC, CVC, CCVC, and CVCC words; **TEKS K.2.B.iv** Identify and read at least 25 high-frequency words from a research-based list. **ELPS 4.C.iv Reading; 4.D.i Reading**

63

Short a and Consonant Ss

 Read

 at

 am

 Sam

 sat

TEKS K.2.B.ii Use letter-sound relationships to decode, including VC, CVC, CCVC, and CVCC words.

64

Directions Remind students that the letter *s* can make the sound /s/ and that the letter *a* can make the sound /a/. Have students take turns decoding the VC and CVC words using letter-sound relationships. Say: Point to each letter in the word and say the sound it makes. Then say the sounds together to read the word.

Short a and Consonant Ss

 MY TURN (Circle) and <u>underline</u>

I (am) Tam.

I like the <u>sun</u>.

I am Sam.

I like to tap.

⭐ **TEKS K.2.B.ii** Use letter-sound relationships to decode, including VC, CVC, CCVC, and CVCC words. **ELPS 4.C.i Speaking; 4.C.iv Reading**

Directions Have students read the sentences, using letter-sound relationships to decode the VC and CVC words. Model: The sound for *a* is /a/. The sound for *m* is /m/. I will say the sounds together to read the word: /a/ /m/, *am*. Then have them circle the words with short *a* and underline the words with initial *s*.

My Learning Goal

I can read realistic fiction.

SPOTLIGHT ON GENRE

Realistic Fiction

The **plot** is what happens in a story.

Problem	Resolution

TURN and TALK Talk about the problem and the resolution. What did the girl do?

TEKS K.7.C Describe the elements of plot development, including the main events, the problem, and the resolution for texts read aloud with adult assistance. **ELPS 3.B.ii Speaking; 4.G.iii Reading**

66

Directions Read the information and remind students that a story has main events, or events that happen at the beginning, middle, and end. Say: A story also has a problem, or something that needs to be fixed, and a resolution, or how the problem is fixed. Have students describe the problem and resolution in the pictures.

Realistic Fiction
Anchor Chart

Problem

Resolution

The pictures and words in a story tell what happens.

Too Many Places to Hide

Preview Vocabulary

| crawls | peeks | unpacks | plunks |

Read

What questions do you have about this story?

Meet the Author

Antonio Sacre writes books, tells stories, and reads all the time. He has a cat that hides in his sock drawer.

⭐ **TEKS K.5.B** Generate questions about text before, during, and after reading to deepen understanding and gain information with adult assistance. **ELPS 4.C.i Reading**

68

Directions Say: You can ask questions about a story before you read it. Asking and answering questions before, during, and after reading can help you better understand a story and get information. Encourage students to look at the illustration on the title page and generate questions about the story before reading.

Too Many Places to Hide

written by Antonio Sacre ▪ illustrated by Jaime Kim

AUDIO

Audio with Highlighting

ANNOTATE

We just moved from the city.
Boxes are everywhere,
and Poof is gone!

CLOSE READ

What is the problem? <u>Underline</u> the words that name the problem.

Dad said he saw her
in the kitchen earlier.
Poof is not there now!

TEKS K.7.C Describe the elements of plot development, including the main events, the problem, and the resolution for texts read aloud with adult assistance. **ELPS 4.G.iii Reading**

71

Our new home has too
many places to hide!
How will we ever find Poof?

Mateo helps me look.

He crawls way back in the closet.

No Poof.

Mom helps me look.
She peeks under the couch.
No Poof.

CLOSE READ

What questions can you ask about what happens on these pages? Highlight the words that answer the questions.

Mateo unpacks bowls.
Dad plunks down cat food.
I have an idea!

TEKS K.5.B Generate questions about text before, during, and after reading to deepen understanding and gain information with adult assistance.
ELPS 4.G.iii Reading

Mateo hands me a bowl.
Dad helps me fill it with cat food.

CLOSE READ

How does the narrator find Poof? Underline the resolution.

Come, Poof!
Dinnertime!
Here is Poof!

TEKS K.7.C Describe the elements of plot development, including the main events, the problem, and the resolution for texts read aloud with adult assistance. **ELPS 4.G.iii Reading**

Develop Vocabulary

crawls	peeks	unpacks	plunks

MY TURN Draw

TEKS K.3.B Use illustrations and texts the student is able to read or hear to learn or clarify word meanings. **ELPS 2.I.iii Listening; 4.G.iii Reading**

Directions Read the vocabulary words to students. Then have them choose a word and draw a picture to show the meaning of the word.

Check for Understanding

 MY TURN (Circle) and write

[handwritten: MIA ♥ MORA]

1. The events **could** **could not** really happen.

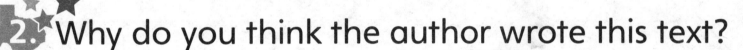

2. Why do you think the author wrote this text?

[handwritten: to tell a story]

3. Poof comes out because

[handwritten: she wants to eat.]

🔷 **TEKS K.6.C** Use text evidence to support an appropriate response. **ELPS 2.I.iii Listening; 4.G.iii Reading; 5.G.iii Writing**

Directions Read item 1 and the answer choices aloud to students. Have them circle the answer. Then read items 2 and 3 and encourage students to write their responses. Remind them to use text evidence.

Read Together

Describe Plot

MY TURN Draw

| Problem | → | Resolution |

TEKS K.7.C Describe the elements of plot development, including the main events, the problem, and the resolution for texts read aloud with adult assistance. **ELPS 2.I.iii Listening; 4.G.iii Reading**

Directions Say: A problem is something in a story that needs to be fixed. A resolution is how the problem is fixed. Have students draw pictures to describe the problem and resolution in the story. Remind them to look back at the text.

Ask and Answer Questions

You can ask questions to help you understand a story or get information.

You can use details in the story to answer your questions.

 Draw

 TEKS K.5.B Generate questions about text before, during, and after reading to deepen understanding and gain information with adult assistance.
ELPS 2.I.iii Listening; ELPS 3.F.i Speaking; ELPS 4.G.iii Reading

Directions Read the information about asking and answering questions. Have students look back at the text. Ask them to share a question they had during reading or generate a new question with a partner. Then have them draw the answer to their question using text details.

Reflect and Share

TURN and TALK Tell about the problem and resolution in the story. How does this plot remind you of other stories you have read?

> You can retell the events in a story.

Weekly Question

What is exciting about moving to a new place?

⭐ **TEKS K.5.E** Make connections to personal experiences, ideas in other texts, and society with adult assistance; **TEKS K.6.B** Provide an oral, pictorial, or written response to a text; **TEKS K.6.D** Retell texts in ways that maintain meaning. **ELPS 4.G.ii Reading; 4.G.iii Reading; ELPS 5.G.iii Writing**

Directions Tell students they read about characters who solve a problem. Have students retell the events in the story, including the problem and resolution. Say: When you retell a story, you tell the important events. Then have them respond to sources by talking about how the plot is similar to other stories they have read.

Read Together

I can use words to tell about stories.

My Learning Goal

Academic Vocabulary

map	move	land	special

 MY TURN (Circle) and <u>underline</u>

move

leave

stay

 TEKS K.6.F Respond using newly acquired vocabulary as appropriate. **ELPS 4.F.iii Reading**

Directions Read the words to students. Ask them to circle the word that has a similar meaning to the word *move*. Have them underline the word that has the opposite meaning.

Concept Sort

 Match

⭐ TEKS K.3.C Identify and use words that name actions; directions; positions; sequences; categories such as colors, shapes, and textures; and locations.
ELPS 2.I.iii Listening; 5.G.iii Writing

Directions Have students identify the picture words on the left as *food* or *not food*. Then have them draw a line to match each picture word on the left to a picture word on the right that belongs in the same category.

Read Like a Writer, Write for a Reader

MKA

 Write

1. Who tells the story? Find words in the text that help you know who tells the story.

me I

2. Write a sentence that tells about an event. Use the word **I**.

I love recess

🌐 **TEKS K.9.E** Listen to and experience first- and third-person texts. **ELPS 2.I.iii Listening; ELPS 4.C.iv Reading**

Directions Say: Sometimes a character is the narrator, or the person telling a story. The narrator uses words such as *I* and *we* to tell the story. Have students listen to and experience first-person text as you read aloud a page from the story. Then read the items one at a time and have students write their responses.

Read Together

Singular Nouns

A **noun** can name a thing or a place.

ball park

 TURN and **TALK** Tell which word names a thing. Tell which word names a place.

 MY TURN Write

yard (bike)

The ___bike___ is in the ___yard___.

⭐ **TEKS K.10.D.iii** Edit drafts with adult assistance using standard English conventions, including singular and plural nouns. **ELPS 4.C.iv Reading; 5.B.ii Writing**

Directions Read the information at the top of the page. Have students identify which noun names a thing and which one names a place. Then have students edit the sentence by writing each singular noun in the correct position in the sentence.

Read Together

WRITING WORKSHOP

My Learning Goal

I can draw or write.

Parts of a Book

Books have a front cover, a back cover, and a title page.

 MY TURN Match

| front cover | back cover | title page |

 TEKS K.2.D.i Identify the front cover, back cover, and title page of a book.

Directions Say: The front cover names the title and author of a book. The title page is the first page in a book. It names the title and author too. The back cover tells details about a book. Ask students to identify the front cover, back cover, and title page by drawing a line from each term to the matching image.

Parts of a Page

A page has **words.** Words tell a story or information.

A page has **pictures.** Pictures show more about the words.

 MY TURN Write and draw

⭐ **TEKS K.9.C** Discuss with adult assistance the author's use of print and graphic features to achieve specific purposes; **TEKS K.10.B** Develop drafts in oral, pictorial, or written form by organizing ideas. **ELPS 5.B.i Writing; 5.B.ii Writing**

 88

Directions Display a book from the classroom library and explain how the author uses print and graphic features, including the main text and pictures, to achieve a specific purpose. Then encourage students to create a page for a book using both words and pictures.

Meet the Author

An **author** is the person who writes a book.

 Write and draw

_____

- - - - - - - - - - - - - - - - - -

_____

TEKS K.10.B Develop drafts in oral, pictorial, or written form by organizing ideas. **ELPS 2.C.iv Listening; 5.B.i Writing; 5.B.ii Writing**

Directions Discuss the author's role in writing a book. Then encourage students to tell about themselves as authors by drawing and writing.

89

National Parks

National parks are special places.
You might see interesting animals.

90

Weekly Question

What makes us want to visit a special place?

You can hike.
What might you
see as you hike?

You can learn about the past.
People lived here long ago.

Talk to your partner about what makes national parks special.

TEKS K.6.E Interact with sources in meaningful ways such as illustrating or writing; **Social Studies TEKS K.5.A** Identify the physical characteristics of place such as landforms, bodies of water, natural resources, and weather. **ELPS 2.I.iii Listening; 3.E.i Speaking**

Directions Read the text to students. Have them interact with the source by looking at the pictures and explaining why national parks are special places.

Sound Parts

SEE and SAY (Circle)

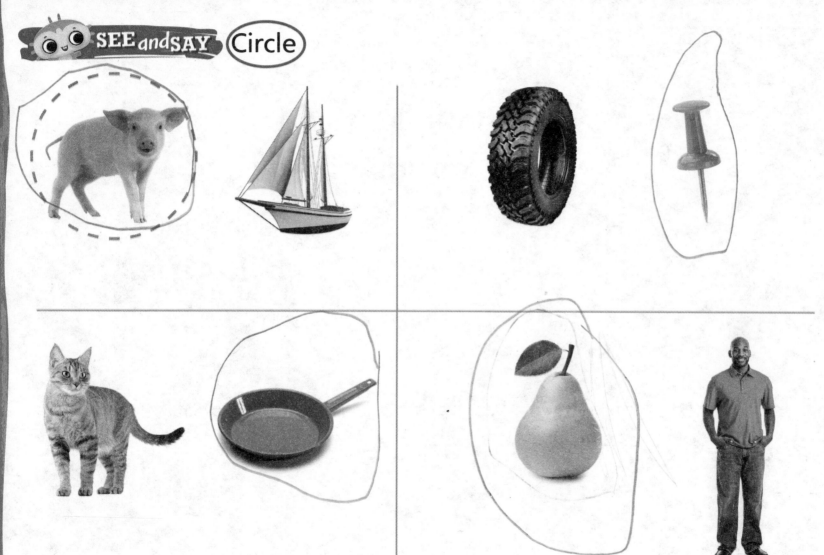

✿ **TEKS K.2.A.vii** Blend spoken onsets and rimes to form simple words. **ELPS 2.I.iii Listening**

92

Directions Have students segment and blend the onset and rime in each picture word. Then have them circle the word in each pair that begins with the sound /p/. Model: Listen to this word: /p/-*ig*, *pig*. The word *pig* begins with the sound /p/.

Consonant Pp

 Write

TEKS K.2.B.i Identify and match the common sounds that letters represent; **TEKS K.2.E** Develop handwriting by accurately forming all uppercase and lowercase letters using appropriate directionality. **ELPS 4.C.i Reading; 5.A.i Writing**

Directions Tell students that the letter *p* stands for the sound /p/. Explain that they will see the letter *p* in many words that begin with the sound /p/. Model how to form the letters *P* and *p*. Then have students say the name of each picture and tell whether the picture word starts with *p*. Say: If the picture word starts with *p*, write the letters. If the picture word does not start with *p*, draw an X over the picture.

Consonant Pp

 MY TURN Read and write

tap · Tap

map · Map

Pam · Pam

TEKS K.2.B.ii Use letter-sound relationships to decode, including VC, CVC, CCVC, and CVCC words. **ELPS 4.C.i Reading; 5.A.i Writing**

Directions Have students name the first picture and tell what letter the picture word ends with. Then ask them to trace the letter in the word. Finally, have students read the word and write it on the lines. Repeat with the remaining pictures and words.

Sound Parts

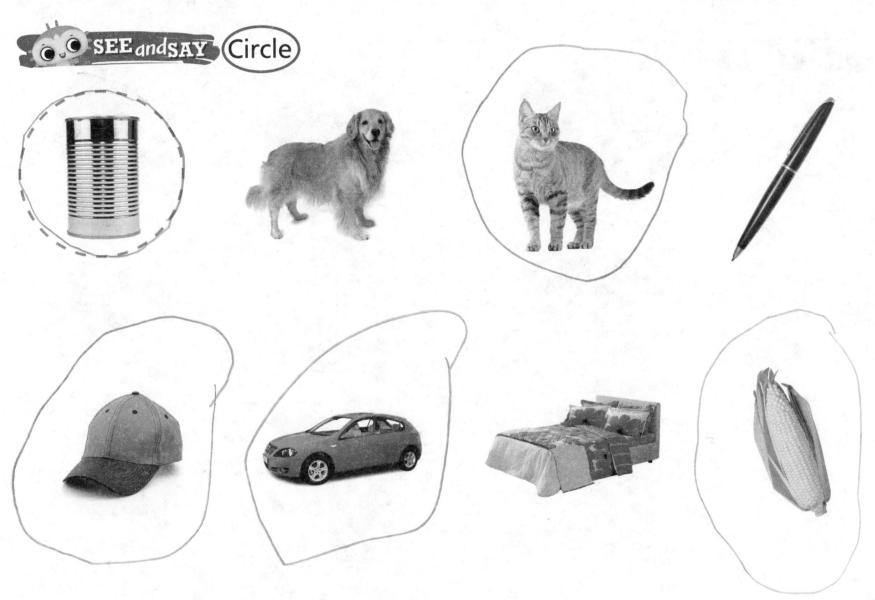

SEE and SAY (Circle)

⊕ **TEKS K.2.A.vii** Blend spoken onsets and rimes to form simple words. **ELPS 2.I.iii Listening**

Directions Name the pictures in the first row with students. Model segmenting and blending onset and rime: Listen to this word: /k/-an, can. Have students segment and blend the onset and rime in the remaining words and circle the picture words that start with /k/. Then have them continue with the second row.

Consonant Cc

TEKS K.2.B.i Identify and match the common sounds that letters represent; **TEKS K.2.E** Develop handwriting by accurately forming all uppercase and lowercase letters using appropriate directionality. **ELPS 4.C.i Reading; 5.A.i Writing**

Directions Tell students that the letter c can make the sound /k/. Model how to form the letters C and c. Say: You will see the letter c in many words that begin with the sound /k/. Trace the letters Cc. Point to the letters and say the sound they can make. Now circle each picture word that begins with the sound for c.

My Words to Know

he	is	have

My Sentences to Read

He is a cat.

I have a map.

TEKS K.2.B.iv Identify and read at least 25 high-frequency words from a research-based list. **ELPS 4.C.i Reading; 4.D.i Reading**

Directions Tell students that the words in the word bank are words they need to practice and remember. Read the words with students as they point to each word. Then have them read the sentences with you and underline the high-frequency words.

Consonant Cc

 MY TURN Read and match

cap

cam

cat

⭐ **TEKS K.2.B.ii** Use letter-sound relationships to decode, including VC, CVC, CCVC, and CVCC words. **ELPS 4.C.i Reading; 5.A.i Writing**

98

Directions Have students trace the letter C or c in each word. Then have them decode the words. Finally, have students draw a line from each word to the matching picture.

The Map

I have a cat.

He is Mac.

🔊 AUDIO

Audio with Highlighting

✏️ ANNOTATE

🔷 **TEKS K.2.B.i** Identify and match the common sounds that letters represent; **TEKS K.2.B.ii** Use letter-sound relationships to decode, including VC, CVC, CCVC, and CVCC words; **TEKS K.2.B.iv** Identify and read at least 25 high-frequency words from a research-based list. **ELPS 4.C.iv** Reading; **4.D.i** Reading

99

I pat Mac.

100

 TEKS K.2.B.i Identify and match the common sounds that letters represent; **TEKS K.2.B.ii** Use letter-sound relationships to decode, including VC, CVC, CCVC, and CVCC words; **TEKS K.2.B.iv** Identify and read at least 25 high-frequency words from a research-based list. **ELPS 4.C.iv Reading; 4.D.i Reading**

Underline the words
with the letter **p**.

Tap the map, Mac.

TEKS K.2.B.i Identify and match the common sounds that letters represent; **TEKS K.2.B.ii** Use letter-sound relationships to decode, including VC, CVC, CCVC, and CVCC words; **TEKS K.2.B.iv** Identify and read at least 25 high-frequency words from a research-based list. **ELPS 4.C.iv Reading; 4.D.i Reading**

Consonants Cc and Pp

 Read

 I am Cam.

 I am Pam.

 I pat the cat.

 I like the cap.

⭐ **TEKS K.2.B.ii** Use letter-sound relationships to decode, including VC, CVC, CCVC, and CVCC words. **ELPS 4.C.iv Reading; 4.D.i Reading**

102

Directions Remind students that the letter *p* makes the sound /p/ and the letter *c* can make the sound /k/. Have partners take turns using letter-sound relationships to decode the VC and CVC words and read the sentences.

Consonants Cc and Pp

 MY TURN (Circle) and <u>underline</u>

I am (Pam).

I have a <u>c</u>at.

I like the cat.

I pat the cat.

 TEKS K.2.B.ii Use letter-sound relationships to decode, including VC, CVC, CCVC, and CVCC words. **ELPS 4.C.iv Reading; 4.D.i Reading**

Directions Remind students that the letter *p* makes the sound /p/ and the letter *c* can make the sound /k/. Have students circle the words with the letter *p* and underline the words with the letter *c*. Then have students take turns reading the sentences with a partner.

My Learning Goal   I can read about special places.

Informational Text

Informational texts tell about real people, places, or things.

Main Idea ⟶ There are many things at the playground.

Details ⟶ There is a slide.

There are swings.

There is a sandbox.

TURN and TALK Talk about how this informational text is different from a realistic fiction story.

⭐ **TEKS K.8.D.i** Recognize characteristics and structures of informational text, including the central idea and supporting evidence with adult assistance. **ELPS 3.B.ii Speaking; 4.G.iii Reading**

Directions Read the genre information and model text to students. Say: The central, or main, idea of an informational text is what the text is mostly about. Supporting evidence, or details, tells more about the main idea. Have students compare and contrast the informational text and realistic fiction stories.

104

Informational Text
Anchor chart

Park

Main Idea

Detail

Detail

Detail

At the Library

Preview Vocabulary

library

librarian

computers

movie

Read

Read the text and look at the pictures to learn why
a library is a special place.

Meet the Author

Eric Braun has written more than one hundred
books, including *If I Were an Astronaut*. He lives in
Minnesota with his wife, two sons, dog, and gecko.

At the Library

written by Eric Braun

AUDIO

Audio with Highlighting

ANNOTATE

The library is a special place.
People can do many things here.

CLOSE READ

What words tell the main idea of the text? <u>Underline</u> the words.

Here are the books.
He can find a good book to read.

TEKS K.8.D.i Recognize characteristics and structures of informational text, including the central idea and supporting evidence with adult assistance. **ELPS 4.G.iii Reading**

Here are the computers.
She can use it to tell a story.

What words tell about the main idea? Highlight the words in the text.

Here are the movies.
They can take a movie home.

111

TEKS K.6.C Use text evidence to support an appropriate response. ELPS 4.G.iii Reading

This is story time.
The children listen to a story.

CLOSE READ

What words tell about the main idea? Highlight the words in the text.

This is a teacher.
She helps students with
their homework.

TEKS K.6.C Use text evidence to support an appropriate response. ELPS 4.G.iii Reading

This is the librarian.
He helps people find books.

The library is a great place!

Develop Vocabulary

 MY TURN Match

library   movie   librarian   computers

TEKS K.3.B Use illustrations and texts the student is able to read or hear to learn or clarify word meanings. ELPS 2.I.iii Listening; 4.G.iii Reading

Directions Say: You can use pictures and words in a text to help you learn the meaning of a new word. Read the vocabulary words to students. Have them go back to the text and discuss the meanings of the words. Then have students use pictures to clarify the meanings of the words by drawing lines from each word to the matching picture.

116

Check for Understanding

 MY TURN Write

1. One way libraries are special is

story time

2. Why did the author write this text?

to tell ysabout libres

3. What does a librarian do?

TEKS K.6.C Use text evidence to support an appropriate response. **ELPS 2.I.iii Listening; 4.G.iii Reading; ELPS 5.B.ii Writing; 4.G.iii Writing**

Directions Read item 1 and encourage students to write an answer. Continue with items 2 and 3. Remind students to use text evidence to support their responses.

Read Together

Find Main Idea

The **central**, or **main**, **idea** is what a text is mostly about.

 MY TURN (Circle) and draw

library	computer

⭐ **TEKS K.8.D.i** Recognize characteristics and structures of informational text, including the central idea and supporting evidence with adult assistance. **ELPS 2.I.iii** Listening; **4.G.iii** Reading

Directions Read the information to students. Have them look back at the text. Ask students to circle the word that tells the main idea. Then have them draw about the main idea.

Use Text Evidence

MY TURN Draw

TEKS K.6.C Use text evidence to support an appropriate response. **ELPS 2.I.iii Listening; 4.G.iii Reading**

Directions Explain that text evidence is the details in a text that support, or tell about, an idea. Say: Think about the main, or central, idea of the text. How do you know this is the main idea? Have students draw two details from the text that support their response on the previous page. Remind them to look back at the text.

Reflect and Share

Weekly Question

What makes us want to visit a special place?

⭐ **TEKS K.5.E** Make connections to personal experiences, ideas in other texts, and society with adult assistance; **TEKS K.6.B** Provide an oral, pictorial, or written response to a text. **ELPS 2.I.iii Listening; 4.G.iii Reading**

Directions Tell students they read about a library. Ask them to think of other special places they have read about. Have them respond to sources by drawing a picture of a library and another place they read about.

Read Together

I can use words to make connections.

Academic Vocabulary

| map | move | land | special |

 MY TURN Write

We use a _map_ to help us find places.

A park is a _spe_____ place.

⭐ **TEKS K.3.B** Use illustrations and texts the student is able to read or hear to learn or clarify word meanings; **TEKS K.6.F** Respond using newly acquired vocabulary as appropriate. **ELPS 4.F.iii Reading**

Directions Read the Academic Vocabulary words to students. Then read the sentences. Have students respond using newly acquired vocabulary by choosing the appropriate words to write on the lines.

Concept Sort

 MY TURN Circle

B

⭐ **TEKS K.3.C** Identify and use words that name actions; directions; positions; sequences; categories such as colors, shapes, and textures; and locations. **ELPS 2.I.iii Listening; 5.G.iii Writing**

122

Directions Say: A category is a group of items that has something in common. We can name the items in a group and then say what they have in common. Have students name the three items in the boxes and identify the category as shapes. Finally, have students circle and say the picture names that belong in the category.

Read Like a Writer, Write for a Reader

 Write

1. Find a word or group of words that tells why the author thinks libraries are special.

booksreadcompulers

2. What other word or group of words can you write to tell why libraries are special?

bookclubandgames

TEKS K.6.C Use text evidence to support an appropriate response. **ELPS 2.I.iii Listening; 3.H.iii Speaking**

Directions Read the first item to students and have them look back at the text to find an answer. Then read the second item. Ask students to write a word or group of words that tells why they think libraries are special.

Plural Nouns

We add **s** to the end of some nouns to name more than one.

1 dog

2 dog**s**

 Tell how many there are of each thing. Which word needs an **s** at the end?

 Circle and write

The two tree are tall.

_____

trees

TEKS K.10.D.iii Edit drafts with adult assistance using standard English conventions, including singular and plural nouns. **ELPS 5.B.ii Writing**

124

Directions Read the information at the top of the page. Have partners count the books and desk in the pictures and discuss which word needs a plural ending. Then read the sentence with students. Have them edit the sentence by circling the word that should end with s. Ask them to write the plural noun on the line.

I can draw or write.

Types of Books

 MY TURN Write and draw

_____

- -

_____

TEKS K.10.B Develop drafts in oral, pictorial, or written form by organizing ideas. **ELPS 5.B.i Writing; 5.B.ii Writing**

Directions Say: Some books tell a story. Some books tell facts. Some books tell how to do something. Have students think about different types of books they have read. Then ask them to create a cover for a book. They should think of a title and a picture that shows what the book is about and what type of book it is.

Spaces Between Words

Letters make up a word.

Words make up a sentence.

There are spaces between the words in a sentence.

 MY TURN (Circle)

Here are the computers.

 MY TURN Write

| **Here** | **are** | **the** | **books.** |

Here are thebooks

TEKS K.2.D.iii Recognize that sentences are comprised of words separated by spaces and recognize word boundaries; **TEKS K.2.D.iv** Recognize the difference between a letter and a printed word. **ELPS 5.F.ii Writing**

Directions Have students recognize the difference between a letter and a word in the sentence by first naming letters they know and then pointing to each word. Ask them to circle the spaces between the words to show word boundaries. Finally, have students use the words in the word bank to write a sentence.

When to Start a New Book

Before you start a new book, make sure the book you are writing is finished. You can use a checklist.

 MY TURN Check

☐ Did you make a title page?

☐ Did you color the pictures?

☐ Can you add more details?

☐ Did you put spaces between the words?

Directions Discuss the items on the checklist with students. Explain that they can use the checklist to help evaluate and revise their own writing.

Exploring the Woods

There is a lot to see in the woods!

You can see trees.

You can see animal homes.

You can see bugs too!

What is fun about exploring new places?

TEKS K.6.E Interact with sources in meaningful ways such as illustrating or writing; **Social Studies TEKS K.5.A** Identify the physical characteristics of place such as landforms, bodies of water, natural resources, and weather. **ELPS 2.I.iii Listening; 3.E.i Speaking**

Directions Read the text to students. Then have them interact with the source by coloring the picture. As they color, have students talk about the things they see in the woods.

Middle Sounds

 Match

 TEKS K.2.A Demonstrate phonological awareness. **ELPS 2.I.iii Listening**

130

Directions Model: Listen to the sounds in the word *pin*: /p/ /i/ /n/. What sound is in the middle? That's right! The sound in the middle is /i/. Have students name the pictures and identify the middle sound in each word. Then ask them to draw a line from each picture word that has the medial sound /i/ to the picture of the pin.

Short i Spelled i

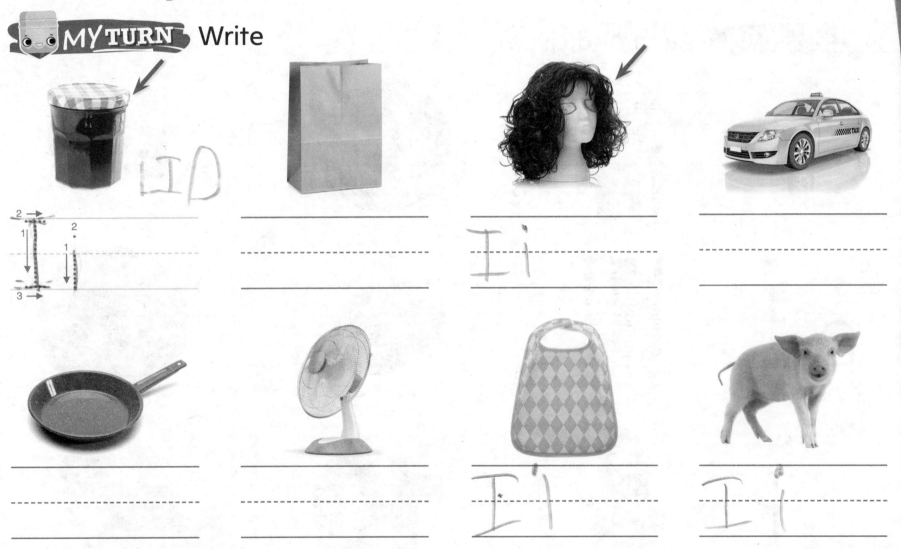

MY TURN Write

LID

I i

I i   I i

TEKS K.2.B.i Identify and match the common sounds that letters represent; **TEKS K.2.E** Develop handwriting by accurately forming all uppercase and lowercase letters using appropriate directionality. **ELPS 4.C.i Reading; 5.A.i Writing**

Directions Tell students that the letter *i* can make the sound /i/. Explain that they will see the letter *i* in many words with the short *i* sound. Model how to form the letters *I* and *i*. Then ask students to say the sounds in each picture word and identify the middle sound. **Say:** If the picture word has the sound /i/ in the middle, write the letters *Ii*.

131

Short i Spelled i

MY TURN Read and circle

s i p

p i t

s i t

⭐ **TEKS K.2.B.ii** Use letter-sound relationships to decode, including VC, CVC, CCVC, and CVCC words. **ELPS 4.C.i Reading**

Directions Have students trace the letter *i* in each word. Then have them read the word and circle the matching picture.

Initial and Final Sounds

SEE and SAY (Circle)

TEKS K.2.A Demonstrate phonological awareness. **ELPS 2.I.iii Listening**

Directions Model: Listen to the sounds in this word: /n/ /e/ /t/, *net*. The word *net* begins with the sound /n/. Have students identify the picture words in the first row and circle the pictures that begin with the sound /n/. Then have students continue with the second row, circling picture words that end with the sound /n/.

133

Consonant Nn

MY TURN (Circle)

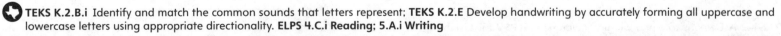

TEKS K.2.B.i Identify and match the common sounds that letters represent; **TEKS K.2.E** Develop handwriting by accurately forming all uppercase and lowercase letters using appropriate directionality. **ELPS 4.C.i Reading; 5.A.i Writing**

Directions Tell students that the letter *n* makes the sound /n/. Say: You will see the letter *n* in many words with the sound /n/. Model how to form the letters *N* and *n*. Have students trace the letters *Nn* in each row and identify the sound the letters make. Then have them circle the picture words that begin or end with the sound for *n*.

My Words to Know

| my | we | make |

My Sentences to Read

I make my pit in the dirt.

We sit in it.

TEKS K.2.B.iv Identify and read at least 25 high-frequency words from a research-based list. **ELPS 4.C.i Reading; 4.D.i Reading**

Directions Say: We have to practice reading some words so we can remember them. Have students read the high-frequency words and then the sentences. Say: Underline the high-frequency words in the sentences.

Consonant Nn

 MY TURN Read and write

pi n   n ap   ca n   ma n

pin   nap   can   man

pin   napcan   man

 136

🔹 **TEKS K.2.B.ii** Use letter-sound relationships to decode, including VC, CVC, CCVC, and CVCC words. **ELPS 4.C.i Reading; 5.A.i Writing**

Directions Ask students to trace the letter *n* in each word and say the picture name. Then have them choose two of the words to read and write on the lines.

In the Pit

Highlight the words with the short **i** sound.

I make a pit.

We can sit in my pit.

AUDIO

Audio with Highlighting

ANNOTATE

TEKS K.2.B.i Identify and match the common sounds that letters represent; **TEKS K.2.B.ii** Use letter-sound relationships to decode, including VC, CVC, CCVC, and CVCC words; **TEKS K.2.B.iv** Identify and read at least 25 high-frequency words from a research-based list. **ELPS 4.C.iv Reading; 4.D.i Reading**

137

Tim can tip a pan.

I can tap a pan.

TEKS K.2.B.i Identify and match the common sounds that letters represent; TEKS K.2.B.ii Use letter-sound relationships to decode, including VC, CVC, CCVC, and CVCC words; TEKS K.2.B.iv Identify and read at least 25 high-frequency words from a research-based list. ELPS 4.C.iv Reading; 4.D.i Reading

<u>Underline</u> the words with the **n** sound.

It is a pin!

TEKS K.2.B.i Identify and match the common sounds that letters represent; **TEKS K.2.B.ii** Use letter-sound relationships to decode, including VC, CVC, CCVC, and CVCC words; **TEKS K.2.B.iv** Identify and read at least 25 high-frequency words from a research-based list. **ELPS 4.C.iv Reading;** **4.D.i Reading**

Short i and Consonant Nn

 TURN and **TALK** Read

pit	**tip**	**pin**
Nan	**nap**	**Nat**
pan	**tan**	**can**
sit	**Tim**	**sip**

TEKS K.2.B.ii Use letter-sound relationships to decode, including VC, CVC, CCVC, and CVCC words. **ELPS 4.C.iv Reading; 4.D.i Reading**

Directions Say: Remember that the letter *i* can make the sound /i/ and the letter *n* makes the sound /n/. Have students take turns reading the words with a partner.

Short i and Consonant Nn

 MY TURN Read and <u>underline</u>

<u>sit</u>   sip

man   ~~nap~~

pit   ~~pin~~

pan   ~~can~~

⭐ **TEKS K.2.B.ii** Use letter-sound relationships to decode, including VC, CVC, CCVC, and CVCC words. **ELPS 4.C.iv Reading; 4.D.i Reading**

Directions Say: Remember that the letter *n* makes the sound /n/ and the letter *i* can make the sound /i/. Read each pair of words and underline the word that names the picture.

My Learning Goal

I can read realistic fiction.

SPOTLIGHT ON GENRE

Realistic Fiction

The **setting** is where and when a story takes place.

TURN and TALK Tell a partner about the setting in the picture.

⭐ **TEKS K.7.D** Describe the setting. **ELPS 3.B.ii Speaking; 4.G.iii Reading**

142

Directions Read the information at the top of the page to students. Then have them work with a partner to describe the setting in the picture, including the time and the place.

Realistic Fiction
Anchor Chart

Place and Time

Setting

Where Is Twister?

Preview Vocabulary

chasing	slips	scrambles	follows

Read

Read to find out who Twister is.

Meet the Author

Bonnie Lass is a teacher who writes stories for beginning readers. She is the author of *Who Took the Cookies from the Cookie Jar?*

144

Where Is Twister?

written by Bonnie Lass
illustrated by Josée Masse

AUDIO

Audio with Highlighting

ANNOTATE

Olivia and Twister are in the barnyard.
Olivia is feeding the chickens.
Twister helps.

CLOSE READ

Where does the story take place? Underline the word.

Olivia looks up.
She thinks, "Where is Twister?"
Twister is chasing a butterfly!

TEKS K.7.D Describe the setting. ELPS 4.G.iii Reading

Twister stops. Where is he?
Twister is in the woods!

CLOSE READ

What detail does the text tell about the woods? Highlight the words.

There are lots of sticks here.
Twister finds a good one to chew on.

149

TEKS K.5.H Synthesize information to create new understanding with adult assistance. **ELPS 4.G.iii Reading**

Chewing makes Twister thirsty.
He finds a creek and has a drink.

CLOSE READ

What detail does the text tell about the woods? Highlight the words.

Twister slips and falls in!
Twister is scared.

TEKS K.5.H Synthesize information to create new understanding with adult assistance. **ELPS 4.G.iii Reading**

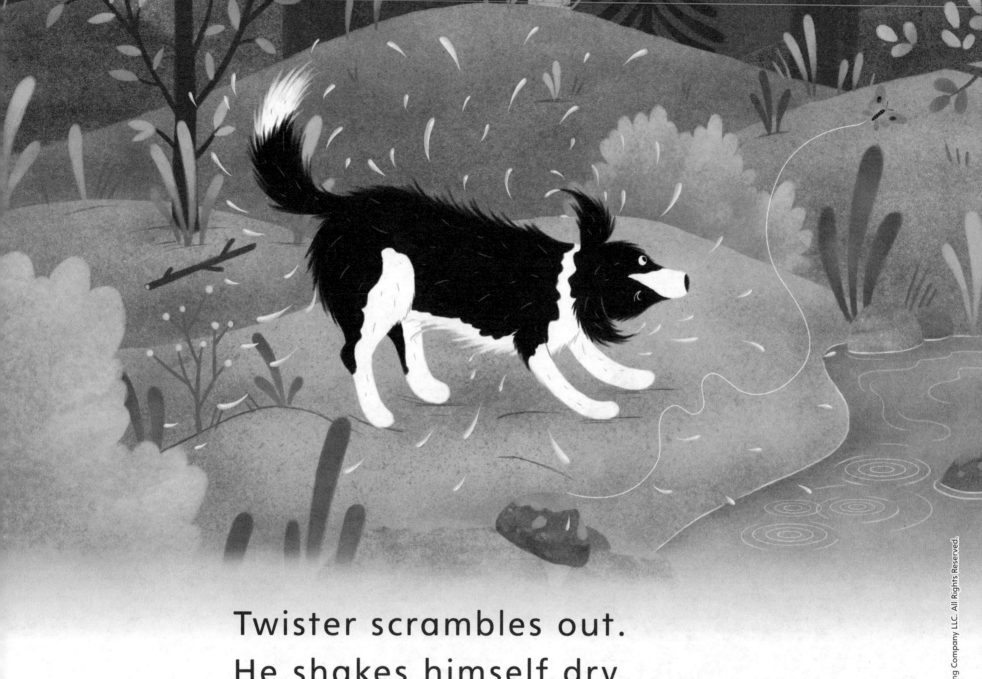

Twister scrambles out.
He shakes himself dry
in the sunshine.
Look! There is the butterfly!

CLOSE READ

When does the story take place? Underline the clue.

Twister follows the butterfly home.
"Twister!" says Olivia.
"You came back to me!"

TEKS K.7.D Describe the setting. **ELPS 4.G.iii Reading**

Develop Vocabulary

 MY TURN Write

| slips | follows | chasing | scrambles |

Twister starts ___CHOSing___ a butterfly.

Copyright © Savvas Learning Company LLC. All Rights Reserved.

⭐ **TEKS K.3.B** Use illustrations and texts the student is able to read or hear to learn or clarify word meanings. **ELPS 4.F.ii Reading; 4.G.iii Reading**

Directions Say: The words and pictures in a text can help you learn and understand the meaning of a word. Have students look back at the text and discuss the meanings of the vocabulary words. Then have them use context clues and the illustration to identify which word best completes the sentence. Ask them to write the word on the lines.

Check for Understanding

 MY TURN Write

1. What happens at the end of the story?

Twster follow a burk lix

2. What words help you know how Olivia feels?

sad and happy

3. Do you think Twister will go back into the woods?

Yes to see new things

TEKS K.6.C Use text evidence to support an appropriate response; **TEKS K.7.C** Describe the elements of plot development, including the main events, the problem, and the resolution for texts read aloud with adult assistance. **ELPS 4.G.iii Reading; 5.B.ii Writing; 5.G.iii Writing**

Directions Read the questions and have students write their responses. Remind them to use evidence from the text.

Describe Setting

  MY TURN Circle and write

The **setting** is where and when
a story takes place.

Form daay

156

TEKS K.7.D Describe the setting. ELPS 2.I.iii Listening; 4.G.iii Reading; 5.G.ii Writing

Directions Read aloud the information and ask students to circle the picture that shows the setting at the beginning of the story. Remind them to look back at the text. Then have students write words that describe when and where the story takes place on the lines.

Create New Understandings

You can use details you learn in a story to understand something new.

MY TURN Draw

TEKS K.5.H Synthesize information to create new understanding with adult assistance. **ELPS 2.I.iii** Listening; **4.G.iii** Reading

Directions Read the information to students. Have them synthesize information from the story to draw the woods setting. Remind students to look back at the text. Ask: What did you learn about the woods that you did not know before?

Reflect and Share

 TURN and TALK What is the setting of the story? What other stories have you read that have a similar setting? Talk about the stories.

Weekly Question

What is fun about exploring new places?

★ **TEKS K.5.E** Make connections to personal experiences, ideas in other texts, and society with adult assistance; **TEKS K.6.B** Provide an oral, pictorial, or written response to a text; **TEKS K.6.C** Use text evidence to support an appropriate response. **ELPS 2.I.iii Listening; 3.H.iii Speaking**

Directions Ask students to talk about the setting in the story. Then ask them to respond to sources by talking with a partner about other stories they have read that take place in a similar setting.

158

My Learning Goal

I can use words to tell about stories.

Academic Vocabulary

map	move	land	special

Word parts can be added to words to make new words.

 Underline

The plane <u>landed</u> on the ground.

Tim moves fast.

 TEKS K.6.F Respond using newly acquired vocabulary as appropriate. **ELPS 4.F.iii Reading**

Directions Say: A word part can change the meaning of a word. The ending *-ed* tells about an action that happened in the past. The ending *-s* tells about an action that is happening now. Read the sentences and have students underline the word in each sentence that has a word part added to it.

159

Concept Sort

 MY TURN Circle

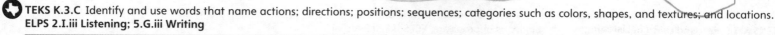
TEKS K.3.C Identify and use words that name actions; directions; positions; sequences; categories such as colors, shapes, and textures; and locations.
ELPS 2.I.iii Listening; 5.G.iii Writing

160

Directions Say: A category is a group of items that has something in common. We can say the items and then identify, or name, the category. Have students name what they see in the three boxes and then identify the category: colors. Then have students circle the pictures in each row that are the same color. Have them talk about other words that would fit in the category.

Read Like a Writer, Write for a Reader

 MY TURN Write

1. Find a word in the text that helps you imagine how Twister feels when he falls into the creek.

Scared

2. What word can you write to help readers picture Twister?

furry

⭐ **TEKS K.9.D** Discuss with adult assistance how the author uses words that help the reader visualize. **TEKS K.9.E** Listen to and experience first- and third-person texts. **ELPS 2.I.iii** Listening

Directions Say: We can experience a story by picturing it in our minds. Read aloud pp. 150–151 as students picture the events in their minds. Then read the first item to students and have them write their answer on the lines. Continue with the second item. Have students discuss their answers.

Plural Nouns

We add **es** to some nouns
to name more than one.

branch

branches

 Write

peach

peach es

 TEKS K.10.D.iii Edit drafts with adult assistance using standard English conventions, including singular and plural nouns. **ELPS 5.D.i Writing**

162

Directions Read to students the information at the top of the page. Then have students look at the pictures at the bottom of the page and read the words. Tell them to edit the word *peach* by changing it to its plural form to match the picture.

My Learning Goal

I can draw or write.

Writing Club

What will you do in Writing Club?

1. You will share your writing.

2. You will talk about your writing.

3. You will listen to others' ideas.

Writing Club will help make you a better writer!

TURN and TALK Introduce yourself to your small group. Then talk about what you want to write about.

TEKS K.1.E Develop social communication such as introducing himself/herself using common greetings and expressing needs and wants. **ELPS 2.I.iii** Listening; **3.D.i** Speaking

Directions Have students develop social communication by introducing themselves using common greetings. Then ask them to practice sharing with others by telling what they want to write about. **Model:** Hello, my name is [name]. I want to write about my trip to the lake.

Ask and Answer Questions

MY TURN Draw

TURN and TALK Answer questions your group asks about your drawing. Ask questions about their drawings.

164

Directions Have students draw about a topic or event. Then ask them to describe their drawing to a small group. Encourage students to ask and answer questions to clarify understanding. Remind them to listen actively to others and to take turns speaking.

Make and Respond to Suggestions

 Draw

 TURN and TALK Share your ideas about your partner's drawing. Listen to your partner's ideas about your drawing.

Directions Say: Sharing and listening to ideas about what we write helps make our writing better. Have students draw a special place and then show their drawing to a partner. Have partners discuss ways they can make their drawings better, such as adding details. Remind them to take turns speaking.

Read Together

What Is in a Neighborhood?

A map shows where places and things are. What special places do you see?

grass
roads
water

PARK

SCHOOL

Weekly Question

How can we describe special places?

MY TURN Match

park

school

playground

TEKS K.6.E Interact with sources in meaningful ways such as illustrating or writing; **Social Studies TEKS K.4.C** Identify tools that aid in determining location, including maps and globes; **TEKS K.15.B** Create and interpret visuals, including pictures and maps. **ELPS 2.I.iii Listening;** **3.E.i Speaking**

Directions Read aloud the text and have students recognize characteristics of a map, such as the map key and symbols. Ask them to interact with the source by talking about the special places they see on the map. Then have students draw lines to match the pictures with the place words.

Alliteration

 Circle

TEKS K.2.A.ii Recognize spoken alliteration or groups of words that begin with the same spoken onset or initial sound. **ELPS 2.I.iii Listening**

168

Directions Say: Some groups of words, such as *tap*, *ten*, and *top*, begin with the same sound. Listen to the words for the pictures in the first row: *cat*, *ball*, *bat*. Which words begin with the same sound? Have students recognize spoken alliteration by circling the picture words in the first row with the same initial sound. Continue with the second row.

Consonant Bb

MY TURN · Circle

TEKS K.2.B.i Identify and match the common sounds that letters represent; **TEKS K.2.E** Develop handwriting by accurately forming all uppercase and lowercase letters using appropriate directionality. **ELPS 4.C.i Reading; 5.A.i Writing**

Directions Tell students that the letter *b* makes the sound /b/. Say: You will see the letter *b* in many words with the sound /b/. Model how to form the letters *B* and *b*. Then have students identify and circle each uppercase *B* and lowercase *b* in the letter jumble. As they circle a letter, ask them to say the sound the letter represents and then trace *B* or *b* on the lines.

Consonant Bb

 MY TURN Read, write, and match

b in   *bir*

b it   *bit*

b at   *bat*

TEKS K.2.B.ii Use letter-sound relationships to decode, including VC, CVC, CCVC, and CVCC words. **ELPS 4.C.i Reading; 5.A.i Writing**

Directions Have students trace the letter *b* in each word. Then have them read the words and write them on the lines. Finally, have students draw a line from each word to the matching picture.

Initial Sounds

⭐ **TEKS K.2.A** Demonstrate phonological awareness. **ELPS 2.I.iii** Listening

Directions Have students say each picture word and circle the items whose names begin with /r/. Model: Listen to this word: *rock*. I hear the sound /r/ at the beginning of *rock*.

Consonant Rr

 MY TURN (Circle)

TEKS K.2.B.i Identify and match the common sounds that letters represent; **TEKS K.2.E** Develop handwriting by accurately forming all uppercase and lowercase letters using appropriate directionality. **ELPS 4.C.i Reading; 5.A.i Writing**

Directions Tell students that the letter *r* makes the sound /r/. Explain that they will see the letter *r* in many words with the sound /r/. Model how to form the letters *R* and *r*. Say: Name the pictures in each row and circle the picture word that begins with the sound /r/. Name the letter that makes the sound. Then trace the letters on the lines.

My Words to Know

| me | for | with |

My Sentences to Read

 MY TURN

Sit with me.

He can bat for me.

⭐ **TEKS K.2.B.iv** Identify and read at least 25 high-frequency words from a research-based list. **ELPS 4.C.i Reading; 4.D.i Reading**

Directions Say: There are some words that we have to remember and practice. Listen as I read these words: *me, for, with*. Have students read the high-frequency words. Then have them read the sentences and identify the high-frequency words by underlining them.

Consonant Rr

 MY TURN Read and write

r a n

_____

r a t

_____

r i p

_____

TEKS K.2.B.ii Use letter-sound relationships to decode, including VC, CVC, CCVC, and CVCC words. **ELPS 4.C.i Reading; 5.A.i Writing**

Directions Have students name each picture and trace the letter *r* in each word. Ask them to read the words. Then have them write the words on the lines.

Ric at Bat

The mitt is for me!

175

TEKS K.2.B.ii Use letter-sound relationships to decode, including VC, CVC, CCVC, and CVCC words; **TEKS K.2.B.iv** Identify and read at least 25 high-frequency words from a research-based list. **ELPS 4.F.i Reading**

Ric is at <u>bat</u>.

He can rip it.

Can I nab it with my mitt?

176

TEKS K.2.B.i Identify and match the common sounds that letters represent; **TEKS K.2.B.ii** Use letter-sound relationships to decode, including VC, CVC, CCVC, and CVCC words; **TEKS K.2.B.iv** Identify and read at least 25 high-frequency words from a research-based list. **ELPS 4.C.iv Reading;** **4.D.i Reading**

Highlight the words with the **r** sound.

Underline the words with the **b** sound.

Ric ran. I sat.

TEKS K.2.B.i Identify and match the common sounds that letters represent; **TEKS K.2.B.ii** Use letter-sound relationships to decode, including VC, CVC, CCVC, and CVCC words; **TEKS K.2.B.iv** Identify and read at least 25 high-frequency words from a research-based list. **ELPS 4.C.iv Reading; 4.D.i Reading**

Consonants Rr and Bb

 MY TURN Write and read

rip

rib

bin

bit

bat

rat

 TEKS K.2.B.ii Use letter-sound relationships to decode, including VC, CVC, CCVC, and CVCC words; **TEKS K.2.B.iii** Recognize that new words are created when letters are changed, added, or deleted such as *it - pit - tip - tap*. **ELPS 4.C.i Reading; 5.A.i Writing**

Directions Have students trace each initial *r* or *b*. Ask them to point to the letters that are different in each pair of words. Then have students decode each word.

Consonants Rr and Bb

 MY TURN (Circle), underline, and match

I like to (rip).

The cat bit it.

He ran with me.

I have a bat.

 TEKS K.2.B.ii Use letter-sound relationships to decode, including VC, CVC, CCVC, and CVCC words. **ELPS 4.C.iv** Reading

Directions Have students read each sentence, underlining words that begin with *b* and circling words that begin with *r*. Then have them match each sentence to the picture that illustrates it.

My Learning Goal I can read about special places.

Informational Text

The purpose of informational texts is to inform.

Purpose — Let me tell you about the library.

Facts — The library has a lot of books.
We do not buy books at a library.
We borrow them.

TURN and TALK Discuss how a story about a library would be different from the informational text.

TEKS K.9.A Discuss with adult assistance the author's purpose for writing text. ELPS 3.B.ii Speaking; 4.G.iii Reading

Directions Read the genre information and the model text to students. Ask them to discuss the purpose of the text. Then have partners contrast a story about a library with the model text.

Informational Text
Anchor Chart

Purpose: to inform about a topic

Fact

Fact

Topic: Cats

Facts tell information about the topic.

Fact

Fact

A Visit to the Art Store

Preview Vocabulary

tools	pencils	brushes	markers

Read

Read the text and look at the pictures to learn about why people go to art stores.

Meet the Author

Jerry Craft has written or drawn pictures for lots of books, including a superhero book that he wrote with his two sons. He also does a newspaper comic strip, and he loves to do school visits!

182

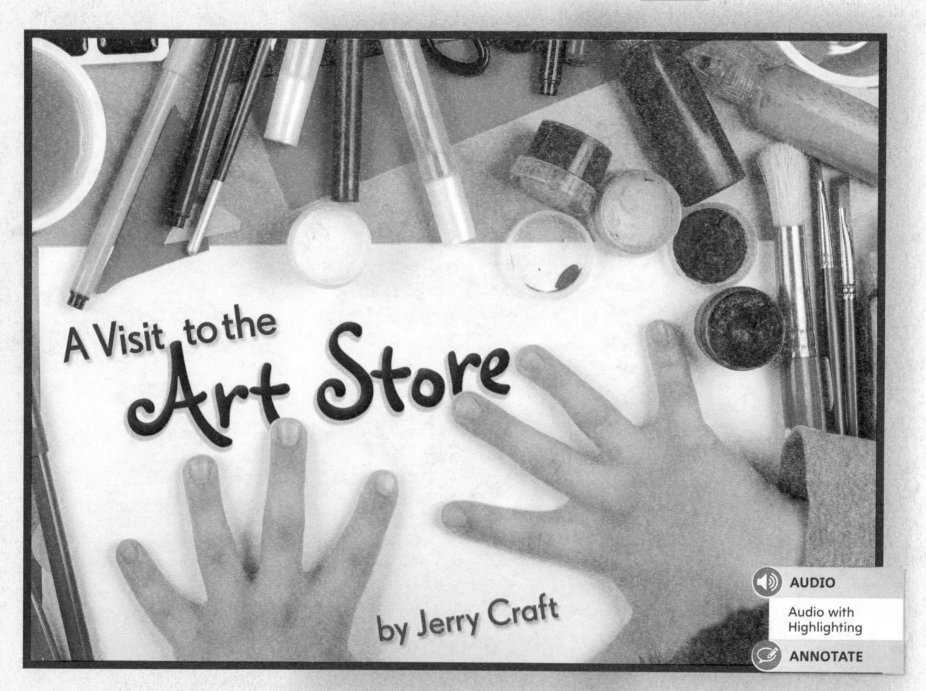

A Visit to the Art Store

by Jerry Craft

AUDIO

Audio with Highlighting

ANNOTATE

Do you want to be an artist?
An art store has the tools you need.

Look at all the artists.
Some artists like to draw.
Some artists like to paint.

Look at all the pencils.
You can make dark lines.
You can make light lines.

CLOSE READ

What does the author tell us we can do with art supplies? <u>Underline</u> things we can do.

Look at all the markers.
You can use every color of the rainbow.

Look at all the paints.
You can use bright colors.
You can use dull colors.

CLOSE READ

What does the author tell us we can do with art supplies? <u>Underline</u> things we can do.

Look at all the brushes.
You can use wide brushes.
You can use thin brushes.

Shopping for art supplies can be a lot of fun.

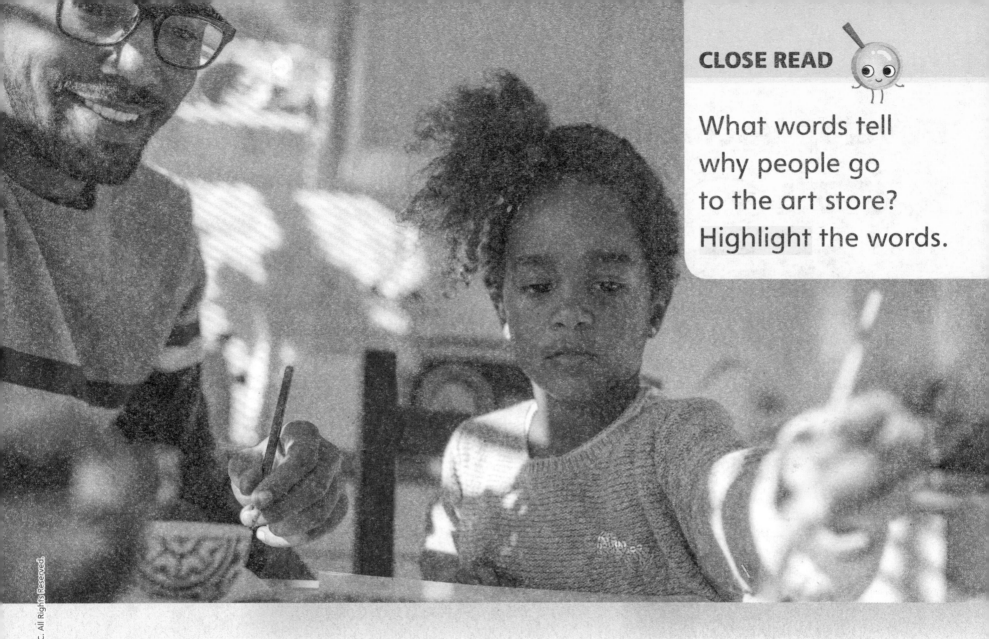

CLOSE READ

What words tell why people go to the art store? Highlight the words.

But using art supplies is even more fun!

TEKS K.5.E Make connections to personal experiences, ideas in other texts, and society with adult assistance. ELPS 4.G.iii Reading

Develop Vocabulary

 MY TURN (Circle)

brushes	(markers)

brushes	pencils

(tools)	brushes

markers	pencils

TEKS K.3.B Use illustrations and texts the student is able to read or hear to learn or clarify word meanings. **ELPS 4.F.iii Reading; 4.F.viii Reading**

Directions Read the words below each picture to students. Have them circle the word that names the picture.

Check for Understanding

 MY TURN Write

1. This text is mostly about

   art store .

 What words help you picture making art with paint?

   bright wide thin

3. What other tools might you find at an art store?

   crayons

⭐ **TEKS K.5.E** Make connections to personal experiences, ideas in other texts, and society with adult assistance; **TEKS K.6.C** Use text evidence to support an appropriate response. **ELPS 4.G.iii Reading; 5.G.iii Writing**

Directions Read the items and have students write their answers. Remind them to use text evidence to support their responses.

Discuss Author's Purpose

The **author's purpose** is the reason an author has for writing.

 Circle

to entertain   to inform

TEKS K.9.A Discuss with adult assistance the author's purpose for writing text. **ELPS 2.I.iii Listening; 3.F.ii Speaking; ELPS 4.F.viii Reading**

194

Directions Read aloud the information at the top of the page. Have students discuss why the author wrote the text and circle the author's purpose. Then have them circle details from the text that support the author's purpose. Remind students to look back at the text.

Make Connections

 Draw

⭐ **TEKS K.5.E** Make connections to personal experiences, ideas in other texts, and society with adult assistance. **ELPS 2.I.iii** Listening; **4.G.iii** Reading

Directions Say: We can connect the ideas we read about with our own community. Have students make connections to society by drawing one reason people might visit an art store in their community. Remind them to look back at the text.

Reflect and Share

TURN and TALK What makes an art store a special place? What makes a library a special place? Tell details from the texts.

You can retell important details.

Weekly Question

How can we describe special places?

TEKS K.5.E Make connections to personal experiences, ideas in other texts, and society with adult assistance; **TEKS K.6.B** Provide an oral, pictorial, or written response to a text; **TEKS K.6.D** Retell texts in ways that maintain meaning. **ELPS 2.I.iii** Listening; **3.B.ii** Speaking

Directions Tell students they read about art stores. Remind them they have also read about libraries. Have partners respond to sources by retelling the texts. Say: When you retell a text, you tell the most important ideas and details.

I can use words to make connections.

My Learning Goal

Academic Vocabulary

| map | move | land | special |

 MY TURN Draw

 TURN and TALK Talk with a partner about your drawing.

⭐ **TEKS K.6.F** Respond using newly acquired vocabulary as appropriate. **ELPS 3.H.iii Speaking**

Directions Have students choose a word that they learned in this unit and draw a picture about the word. Then have them talk with a partner about what they drew and why.

Concept Sort

MY TURN Sort

198

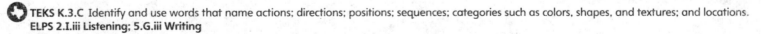

⭐ **TEKS K.3.C** Identify and use words that name actions; directions; positions; sequences; categories such as colors, shapes, and textures; and locations. **ELPS 2.I.iii** Listening; **5.G.iii** Writing

Directions Say: Some of these pictures show toys, and some show objects that are not toys. Sort the pictures by putting the toys in the toy box. Have students draw lines from the pictures of toys to the empty box at the bottom of the page.

Read Like a Writer, Write for a Reader

 MY TURN (Circle) and write

1. Circle the picture that helped you learn more about art stores.

2. How can adding pictures help you as an author?

help show moce

information

Directions Read item 1 to students and have them circle the picture that shows details about an art store. Then read aloud item 2 and have students write their response.

199

Read Together

Singular and Plural Nouns

A **singular noun** names one.

A **plural noun** names more than one.

See the pencil and brush.

See the pencil**s** and brush**es**.

 MY TURN (Circle) and write

I have one dog and two cat.

cats

I love you Dad

foxes

She has three fox.

⭐ **TEKS K.10.D.iii** Edit drafts with adult assistance using standard English conventions, including singular and plural nouns. **ELPS 5.D.i** Writing

Directions Read the information and example sentences to students. Then have students edit the sentences at the bottom of the page. Ask them to circle the words that need a plural ending and write the plural nouns on the lines. Have them identify the singular noun in the sentences.

Read Together

I can draw or write.

My Learning Goal

Edit for Parts of a Book

A book has a **front cover**, a **back cover**, and a **title page**.

 Write

Title

front

Back

 TEKS K.2.D.i Identify the front cover, back cover, and title page of a book. **ELPS 5.B.i Writing; 5.B.ii Writing**

Directions Tell students that the front cover names the title and author of a book, the title page is the first page in the book and also names the title and author, and the back cover tells details about the book. Then ask students to identify the front cover, back cover, and title page by writing the correct term below each picture.

Incorporate Peer Feedback

 MY TURN Draw

⭐ **TEKS K.10.C** Revise drafts by adding details in pictures or words. **ELPS 3.E.i Speaking**

202

Directions Have students talk with a partner about the picture and take turns suggesting details they can add to make it better. Then ask students to work independently to revise the picture by adding details. Encourage them to include details their partner suggested.

How to Celebrate

- ☐ Speak loudly and clearly.
- ☐ Use complete sentences.
- ☐ Listen actively.
- ☐ Ask questions.

TURN and TALK Share your writing with a partner.

Directions Discuss the list of speaking and listening rules with students. Then have them share their writing with a partner.

UNIT THEME

Going Places

 TURN *and* **TALK**

Go back to each text and tell one detail about a special place. Use the Weekly Questions to help you.

BOOK CLUB

At the Library

WEEK 3

What makes us want to visit a special place?

WEEK 2

Too Many Places to Hide

What is exciting about moving to a new place?

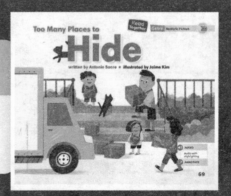

BOOK CLUB

WEEK 1

Mission Accomplished!

How does imagination make a place seem different?

204

Read Together

WEEK 6

B☆OK CLUB

WEEK 4

Where Is Twister?

What is fun about exploring new places?

B☆OK CLUB

WEEK 5

A Visit to the Art Store

How can we describe special places?

B☆OK CLUB

Essential Question

What makes a place special?

Project

WEEK 6

Now it is time to apply what you learned about going places in your **WEEK 6 PROJECT: Let's Go!**

TEKS K.5.H Synthesize information to create new understanding with adult assistance: **TEKS K.6.C** Use text evidence to support an appropriate response. **ELPS 4.F.vii Reading**

Short a Word Families

  Write

pan

con

man

cat

Rax

bat

★ **TEKS K.2.B.i** Identify and match the common sounds that letters represent. **ELPS 5.A.i Writing; 5.C.iii Writing**

Directions Have students say the word for each picture and segment the sounds before writing the word on the lines. **Model:** Listen to the sounds in *pan:* /p/ /a/ /n/. The letter for /p/ is *p*. The letter for /a/ is *a*. The letter for /n/ is *n*.

My Words to Know

she	see	look

My Sentences to Read

1. I <u>see</u> Nat.

2. She is at the mat.

3. Look! It is in the can!

TEKS K.2.B.iv Identify and read at least 25 high-frequency words from a research-based list. **ELPS 4.C.i Reading; 4.D.i Reading**

Directions Have students read the high-frequency words and then the sentences. Ask them to underline the high-frequency words in the sentences.

Short i Word Families

 Write

tin

Pin

bin

tip

sip

Rip

TEKS K.2.B.i Identify and match the common sounds that letters represent. ELPS 5.A.i Writing; 5.C.iii Writing

Directions Have students say the word for each picture and segment the sounds before writing the word on the lines. Ask them to identify the letters and sounds that are the same and different in each set of words.

We Like It!

Highlight the words that are in the same word family as **fin**.

Tim can see a pin.

Look! It is in the bin.

 AUDIO

Audio with Highlighting

 ANNOTATE

209

TEKS K.2.B.ii Use letter-sound relationships to decode, including VC, CVC, CCVC, and CVCC words; **TEKS K.2.B.iv** Identify and read at least 25 high-frequency words from a research-based list. **ELPS 4.C.iv Reading; 4.D.i Reading**

Pat can <u>tap</u> with a bat.

She can rap with Nat.

 TEKS K.2.B.ii Use letter-sound relationships to decode, including VC, CVC, CCVC, and CVCC words; **TEKS K.2.B.iv** Identify and read at least 25 high-frequency words from a research-based list. **ELPS 4.C.iv Reading; 4.D.i Reading**

<u>Underline</u> words that are in the same word family as **cap.**

We sit for a nap.

 TEKS K.2.B.ii Use letter-sound relationships to decode, including VC, CVC, CCVC, and CVCC words; **TEKS K.2.B.iv** Identify and read at least 25 high-frequency words from a research-based list. **ELPS 4.C.iv Reading; 4.D.i Reading**

Let's Go!

Look at the pictures. Which type of museum do you want to go to?

COLLABORATE Talk about museums.

⭐ **TEKS K.6.E** Interact with sources in meaningful ways such as illustrating or writing. **ELPS 2.I.iii** Listening; **3.E.i** Speaking

Directions Read aloud the prompt. Say: A museum is a place where interesting things are collected for people to see. Have students discuss the museums in the pictures and what people can see at the museums. Then have students circle the museums they have visited or museums they would like to visit.

Use Words

 COLLABORATE What questions can you ask about museums? Talk with your partner. Use new academic words.

Museum Research Plan

Check each box as you do your work.

☐ Research the museums.

☐ Choose which one you want to go to.

☐ Draw or write to tell why.

☐ Share with others.

TEKS K.6.F Respond using newly acquired vocabulary as appropriate; **TEKS K.12.A** Generate questions for formal and informal inquiry with adult assistance; **TEKS K.12.B** Develop and follow a research plan with adult assistance. **ELPS 2.I.iii Listening; 3.D.ii Speaking**

Directions Have students generate questions about museums using newly acquired vocabulary. Then discuss the steps in this week's research plan. Explain that students will follow the research plan as they complete their project.

Fact and Opinion

A **fact** is a detail that can be proved to be true.

An **opinion** is what the author thinks or feels.

You should go to a history museum!

You can see dinosaurs.

TEKS K.8.E Recognize characteristics of persuasive text with adult assistance and state what the author is trying to persuade the reader to think or do. **ELPS 2.C.iv** Listening; **4.G.iii** Reading

Directions Say: The author of an opinion text wants to convince readers to think or do something. The author tells an opinion. The author uses facts to support the opinion. Read the sentences below the pictures to students. Have them circle the sentence that tells a fact and underline the sentence that tells an opinion.

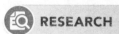
Ask a Librarian

🔍 **RESEARCH**

You can find information in a library.

A librarian can help you!

COLLABORATE Circle who can help you in a library. Talk about questions you can ask.

⭐ **TEKS K.1.E** Develop social communication such as introducing himself/herself using common greetings and expressing needs and wants; **TEKS K.12.A** Generate questions for formal and informal inquiry with adult assistance. **ELPS 2.I.iii Listening; 3.D.ii Speaking**

Directions Say: What do you want to know about your topic? Think of questions you can ask. Asking librarians questions helps them know what you need and want. For example, say, *Hello. Where may I find books about museums?* Have students circle the librarian in the picture. Then have them generate questions for their inquiry project. Tell them to express their needs and wants.

Take Notes

What can you see?

You can learn about
animals from the past.

 COLLABORATE Draw what you can see at each museum.

⭐ **TEKS K.12.C** Gather information from a variety of sources with adult assistance. **ELPS 4.G.iv Reading**

Directions Discuss the research model with students. Say: You can gather, or get, information about art and history museums by looking at books. Have students gather information from a variety of books about art and history museums. Ask them to draw notes about what they can see at each type of museum.

Tell Your Opinion

 RESEARCH

You can draw and write to tell your opinion.

  COLLABORATE Circle the museum you like better.

 COLLABORATE Draw

TEKS K.10.B Develop drafts in oral, pictorial, or written form by organizing ideas. **ELPS 2.I.iii Listening; 4.G.iii Reading**

Directions Remind students that an opinion is what they think or feel about a topic. Read aloud the information and have students circle the picture that shows the type of museum they would rather visit. Then have them draw a picture to show what they learned about the museum they chose.

Share

Follow the rules for speaking and listening.

Speak loudly.

Listen carefully.

Reflect

 Circle

Did I work well with others?

Did I like my project?

TEKS K.1.E Develop social communication such as introducing himself/herself using common greetings and expressing needs and wants;
TEKS K.12.E Use an appropriate mode of delivery, whether written, oral, or multimodal, to present results. **ELPS 2.I.iii Listening; 3.H.iii Speaking**

Directions Say: You can share your project in different ways. You can show your writing, talk about your project, and show pictures. Tell students to choose an appropriate mode of delivery to present their project. Then have them reflect on their project by answering the questions.

Reflect on Your Reading

 Write

I Think

Reflect on Your Writing

 Write

My favorite writing is

TEKS K.6.A Describe personal connections to a variety of sources. **ELPS 5.G.iii Writing**

Directions Have students share their ideas about their reading and writing.

How to Use a Picture Dictionary

school

This is a picture of the word.

This is the word you are learning.

 MY TURN Draw

Directions Say: You can use a picture dictionary to find words. The words are grouped into topics. The topic of this picture dictionary is **locations**. Listen as I read the words. The pictures will help you understand the meanings of the words. Have students identify the word *farm* in the picture dictionary and use it in a sentence. Then have them draw a picture of what the word means.

Locations

playground

farm

city

home

store

How to Use a Glossary

The word is in dark type.

Cc   **circle** A **circle** is a perfectly round line.

All words that begin with the letter C will be after Cc.

This sentence will help you understand what the word means.

 Draw

TEKS K.3.A Use a resource such as a picture dictionary or digital resource to find words. **ELPS 2.I.iii Listening; 4.C.iii Reading**

Directions Say: A glossary can help you find the meanings of words you do not know. The words in a glossary are in alphabetical, or ABC, order. Have students find the word *tools* and draw a picture of the word.

Bb

brushes **Brushes** are tools used for painting.

Cc

chasing When you are **chasing** something, you are running after it to catch it.

circle A **circle** is a perfectly round line.

computers **Computers** are electronic machines.

crawls Someone who **crawls** moves on his or her hands and knees.

cube A **cube** is a solid object with six square sides.

Ff

follows When someone **follows** something, he or she goes after it.

Ll

land **Land** is the solid part of the earth's surface.

librarian A **librarian** is a person who helps at a library.

library A **library** is a place where books and other things are kept for people to borrow.

Mm

map A **map** is a drawing that shows where things are located.

markers **Markers** are tools with colorful ink used for writing or drawing.

move When you **move**, you change the place where you live.

movie A **movie** is a story that is told with moving pictures.

Pp

peeks When someone **peeks**, he or she looks quickly at someone or something.

225

pencils Pencils are pointed tools used for writing or drawing.

plunks When someone **plunks** something down, he or she sets it down hard.

Ss

scrambles When someone **scrambles**, he or she moves or climbs quickly.

slips Someone who **slips** loses his or her balance and slides.

special When something is **special**, it is very important.

square A **square** is a shape with four equal sides.

Tt

tools **Tools** are objects a person uses to do a job or activity.

triangle A **triangle** is a shape with three sides and three corners.

Uu

unpacks When someone **unpacks**, he or she takes things out of a container.

ACKNOWLEDGMENTS

Photographs

Photo locators denoted as follows Top (T), Center (C), Bottom (B), Left (L), Right (R), Background (Bkgd)

6 Shalom Ormsby/Blend Images/Getty Images; 7 Soleg/iStock/Getty Images Plus/Getty Images; 8 (BL) Dmitry Bruskov/Shutterstock, (Bkgd) Suzanne Tucker/Shutterstock; 9 (T) Shalom Ormsby/Blend Images/Getty Images, (B) Soleg/iStock/Getty Images Plus/Getty Images; 10 Umarazak/Shutterstock; 13 Chuyuss/Shutterstock; 14 (BL) Sean Locke Photography/Shutterstock, (C) Macrovector/Shutterstock, (CL) Sean Locke Photography/Shutterstock, (T) Aphelleon/Shutterstock, (TR) Alex Mit/Shutterstock; 15 (BR) Monkey Business Images/Shutterstock, (TL) Sergeydv/123RF; 16 (BCL) Eurobanks/Shutterstock, (BCR) Tritooth/123RF, (BL) Triff/Shutterstock, (BR) Steshkin Yevgeniy/Shutterstock, (TCL) Deep OV/Shutterstock, (TCR) Igor Terekhov/123RF, (TL) Tsekhmister/Shutterstock, (TR) Africa Studio/Shutterstock; 17 (BC) Carolina K. Smith MD/Shutterstock, (BL) Threeseven/Shutterstock, (BR) Kiri11/Shutterstock, (C) Ludmilafoto/Shutterstock, (CL) Apopium/Fotolia, (CR) Pakowacz/Shutterstock, (TC) Everything/Shutterstock, (TL) Eurobanks/Shutterstock, (TR) Everything/Shutterstock; 18 (BR) Eric Isselee/Shutterstock, (TL) Tsekhmister/Shutterstock, (TR) Stockagogo/Craig Barhorst/Shutterstock, (BL) Africa Studio/Shutterstock; 19 (BL) Domnitsky/Shutterstock, (BR) Lisa A. Svara/Shutterstock, (TCL) Philipimage/Shutterstock, (TCR) Vitalii Tiahunov/123RF, (TL) Tarasov/Shutterstock, (TR) Africa Studio/Shutterstock; 20 (BC) DenisNata/Shutterstock, (BL) Triff/Shutterstock, (BR) Igor Terekhov/123RF, (TC) Bluehand/Shutterstock, (TL) Pongsakorn Chaina/Shutterstock, (TR) Africa Studio/Shutterstock; 22 (BC) 123RF, (BL) Eric Isselee/Shutterstock, (BR) Robyn Mackenzie/123RF, (TC) Sergio Schnitzler/Shutterstock, (TL) Philipimage/Shutterstock, (TR) Nick Biebach/123RF; 26 (BR) Pakhnyushcha/Shutterstock, (BL) Philipimage/Shutterstock, (BC) Pongsakorn Chaina/Shutterstock, (TC) Eurobanks/Shutterstock, (TR) Africa Studio/Shutterstock, (TL) Pakowacz/Shutterstock; 27 (TR) Eric Isselee/Shutterstock, (BR) Tsekhmister/Shutterstock, (BCR) Eric Isselee/Shutterstock, (TCR) Arogant/Shutterstock; 45 (BR) BCFC/Shutterstock, (CR) Voyagerix/Shutterstock; 46 (BC) Triff/Shutterstock, (TR) 123RF, (TC) Eric Isselee/Shutterstock, (TL) Roblan/123RF; 48 (L) 123RF, (R) Lisa A. Svara/Shutterstock; 50 (BCL) Monkey Business Images/Shutterstock, (BCR) Wavebreakmedia/Shutterstock, (BL) Racorn/Shutterstock, (BR) Rob Marmion/Shutterstock; 52 (T) Johavel/Shutterstock, (CR) Zoonar GmbH/Alamy Stock Photo, (BL) OJO Images Ltd/Alamy Stock Photo; 53 (R) 123RF, (C) Monkey Business Images/Shutterstock, (L) Anna Krestiannykova/Shutterstock; 54 (BCL) Morena Valente/Shutterstock, (BCR) Tim Large/Shutterstock, (BL) DenisNata/Shutterstock, (TCR) Alex Staroseltsev/Shutterstock, (TL) Lisovskaya Natalia/Shutterstock, (TR) Paul Orr/Shutterstock, (TCL) Everything/Shutterstock, (BR) Lisa A. Svara/Shutterstock; 55 (BL) Room27/Shutterstock, (BR) Deep OV/Shutterstock, (CL) Apopium/Fotolia, (CR) Eric Isselee/Shutterstock, (TL) Thomas Soellner/Shutterstock, (TR) Eurobanks/Shutterstock; 56 (BL) DenisNata/Shutterstock, (CL) Anton Starikov/123RF, (TL) Pakowacz/Shutterstock; 57 (BCL) Africa Studio/Shutterstock, (BCR) Morenina/Shutterstock, (BL) Sergiy1975/Shutterstock, (BR) Dny3d/Shutterstock, (TCL) Adisa/Shutterstock, (TCR) Number 650371/Shutterstock, (TL) Triff/Shutterstock, (TR) Africa Studio/Shutterstock; 58 (BC) Morena Valente/Shutterstock, (BL) Bluehand/Shutterstock, (BR) Phant/Shutterstock, (C) Roblan/123RF, (CL) Triff/Shutterstock, (CR) Kirsanov Valeriy Vladimirovich/Shutterstock, (TC) Ruslan Semichev/Shutterstock, (TL) Ivaschenko Roman/Shutterstock, (TR) Sergey Peterman/Shutterstock; 60 (C) Blaj Gabriel/Shutterstock, (T) Oliver Hoffmann/Shutterstock; 65 (T) Triff/Shutterstock, (B) Celig/Shutterstock; 83 Monkey Business Images/Shutterstock; 84 (CR) LorenzoArcobasso/Shutterstock, (TL) Alex Staroseltsev/Shutterstock, (CL) Kiri11/Shutterstock, (TR) StudioVin/Shutterstock; 86 (BR) TinnaPong/Shutterstock, (TC) Irin-k/Shutterstock, (TR) HelloRF Zcool/Shutterstock; 90 (Bkgd) Hikrcn/123RF, (BL) Jan Miko/Shutterstock, (BR) Sam74100/123RF, (TR) Wollertz/Shutterstock; 91 (CR) Ian Dagnall/Alamy Stock Photo, (TL) Juice Images/Alamy Stock Photo; 92 (BCL) Paul Orr/Shutterstock, (BCR) Maks Narodenko/Shutterstock, (BL) Deep OV/Shutterstock, (BR) Eurobanks/Shutterstock, (TCL) Nerthuz/Shutterstock, (TCR) Tarasov/Shutterstock, (TL) Fotomaster/Fotolia, (TR) Alexander Dashewsky/Shutterstock; 93 (BC) 123RF, (BL) Lem/Shutterstock, (BR) Ozaiachin/123RF, (TC) StudioVin/Shutterstock, (TR) Bokeh Blur Background Subject/Shutterstock, (TL) Fotomaster/Fotolia; 94 (BL) 123RF, (CL) Pakowacz/Shutterstock, (TL) Celig/Shutterstock; 95 (BCL) Adisa/Shutterstock, (BCR) Room27/Shutterstock, (BR) Danny Smythe/Shutterstock, (TCR) Deep OV/Shutterstock, (TL) Testing/Shutterstock, (TR) Phant/Shutterstock, (BL) Everything/Shutterstock, (TCL) Lisa A. Svara/Shutterstock; 96 (BC) Deep OV/Shutterstock, (BL)

Shutterstock, (TC) Maxx-Studio/Shutterstock, (BR) Juthamat98/
Shutterstock, (TL) Bogdan Florea/Shutterstock; **199** (CL) Bernard
Bodo/123RF, (CR) George Rudy/Shutterstock; **200** (BR) Taddeus/
Shutterstock, (CR) Tatiana Popova/Shutterstock, (TR) StudioVin/
Shutterstock; **204** Shalom Ormsby/Blend Images/Getty Images; **206**
(BC) Pakhnyushcha/Shutterstock, (BL) Deep OV/Shutterstock, (BR)
Room27/Shutterstock, (TC) Testing/Shutterstock, (TL) Paul Orr/
Shutterstock, (TR) Eurobanks/Shutterstock; **208** (BR) Kim
Reinick/123RF, (BC) Mikkel Bigandt/Shutterstock, (BL) Alexander
Dashewsky/Shutterstock, (TC) Africa Studio/Shutterstock, (TL)
123RF, (TR) Arina Zaiachin/123RF; **212** (BL) Picture Partners/Alamy
Stock Photo, (BR) Incamerastock/Alamy Stock Photo, (TL) Look Die
Bildagentur der Fotografen GmbH/Alamy Stock Photo; **215**
Wavebreak Media Ltd/123RF; **216** Viktor Schnur/Alamy Stock
Photo; **217** (BR) Picture Partners/Alamy Stock Photo, (L) Look Die
Bildagentur der Fotografen GmbH/Alamy Stock Photo; **220**
Stevegeer/iStock/Getty Images Plus/Getty Images; **221** (BL) MaxyM/
Shutterstock, (BR) Kondor83/Shutterstock, (CR) Radius Images/
Alamy Stock Photo, (TL) Jack Schiffer/Shutterstock, (TR) Jorg
Hackemann/Shutterstock; **223** (B) Hongqi Zhang/123RF, (T)
Gennadiy Poznyakov/123RF; **225** Pakowacz/Shutterstock; **226**
Flotsam/Shutterstock.

Illustrations
12, 21, 23–25, 97, 99–101, 103, 173, 175–177 Jenny B. Harris; **29, 51,
67, 87, 105, 143, 181** Tim Johnson; **31–39, 42** Kevin Zimmer; **59–63,
135, 137–139, 297, 209–211** Nomar Perez; **66, 102–103, 142** Laura
Zarrin; **69–77** Jaime Kim; **129** Nick Diggory; **145–153, 158** Josée
Masse; **166–167** André Jolicoeur; **214, 216** Ken Bowser